Mathematics Enhancement Prog
Demonstration Project

Practice Book: Y9B

Principal Author: Ted Graham, Centre for Teaching Mathematics, Plymouth University

Senior Editor: David Burghes, Centre for Innovation in Mathematics Teaching

Advisors and Checkers: Graham Bryant, Chris Graddon, Chris Hall, David Lee,
                    Graham Middleton, Nigel Oates, Albine Patterson

Typesetter: Liz Holland

This is one component of MEP Mathematics resources for Y9.

All enquiries regarding these resources should be addressed to

Mathematics Enhancement Programme
CIMT, Institute of Education
Plymouth University   Tel: 01752 585346
Plymouth PL4 8AA   Fax: 01752 586520

First printing   February 2001

Published by **CIMT, Plymouth University**

Copyright © CIMT, Plymouth University

Design by *Clinton Banbury*
P.O. Box 2892, Billericay, Essex CM11 2LF
Tel: 01277 630421

Contents

9 Area, Perimeter and Volume

9.1 2-D Shapes

The following table gives the names of some 2-D shapes. In this section we will consider the properties of some of these shapes.

Rectangle		All angles are right angles (90°) Opposite sides have the same length
Square		All the sides have the same length All angles are right angles (90°)
Parallelogram		Opposite sides have the same length
Rhombus		All the sides have the same length Diagonals bisect at right angles
Trapezium		
Kite		Diagonals intersect at right angles
Isosceles Triangle		Two sides have the same length and the angles opposite these two sides are equal
Equilateral Triangle		All angles are 60°

Example 1

Draw the lines of symmetry of an equilateral triangle.

Solution

There are 3 lines of symmetry, as shown in the diagram. They join each vertex (corner) to the midpoint of the opposite side.

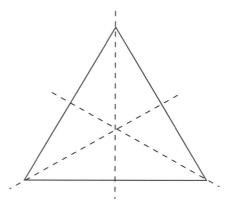

Example 2

Name each of the following shapes:

(a)

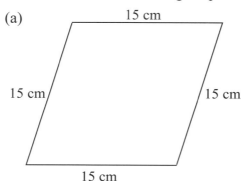

(b)

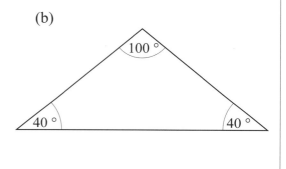

Solution

(a)   This is a *rhombus* because all the sides have the *same* lengths.

(b)   This is an *isosceles triangle* because two of the angles are the same size.

Example 3

State the order of rotational symmetry of:

(a)   a *trapezium,*   (b)   a *parallelogram.*

Solution

(a)   1

(b)   2 (unless the parallelogram happens to be a square, in which case the order of rotational symmetry would be 4).

Exercises

1. Name each of the following shapes:

(a)

6 cm

4 cm

(b)

5 cm

5 cm   5 cm

5 cm

(c)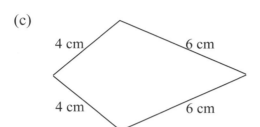

4 cm   6 cm

4 cm   6 cm

(d)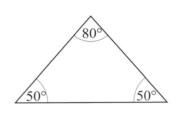

80°

50°   50°

(e)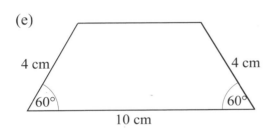

4 cm   4 cm

60°   60°

10 cm

(f)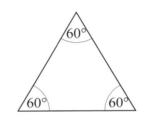

60°

60°   60°

2. Draw diagrams to show the lines of symmetry of:

(a) a *kite,*   (b) a *square,*

(c) a *rectangle,*   (d) an *isosceles triangle.*

3. How many lines of symmetry are there for:

(a) a *parallelogram,*   (b) a *rhombus* ?

4. State whether each of the following statements is *true* or *false.*

(a) A *square* is also a *rhombus.*

(b) A *square* is also a *kite.*

(c) A *rectangle* is also a *kite.*

(d) A *parallelogram* is also a *kite.*

(e) A *rectangle* is also a *parallelogram.*

5. Write down the order of rotational symmetry of:

(a) a *rhombus,*   (b) a *square,*

(c) an *isosceles triangle,* (d) an *equilateral triangle,*

(e) a *kite.*

6.   A triangle has *one* line of symmetry. What type of triangle is it?

7.   Draw a trapezium that has:

       (a)   *one* line of symmetry,   (b)   *no* lines of symmetry.

8.   A right-angled triangle is also an *isosceles* triangle. What sizes are the other angles in this triangle?

9.   For a semicircle:

       (a)   draw a diagram to show its lines of symmetry,

       (b)   state its order of rotational symmetry.

10.   (a)   Draw a diagram to show the lines of symmetry of a *regular pentagon*.

       (b)   State the order of rotational symmetry of a *regular octagon*.

11.   Rosemary drew these rectangles using a computer:

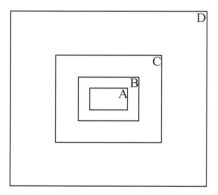

Rectangle A has *width 3* and *length 5*:

The computer repeated these instructions to draw the other rectangles:

       new *width* = previous *width* × 2

       new *length* = previous *length* + previous *width*

Copy and complete this table.

	width	length
rectangle A	3	5
rectangle B	......	......
rectangle C	......	......
rectangle D	......	......

(KS3/94/Ma/3-5/P1)

9.2 Area of Special Shapes

In this section we calculate the area of various shapes.

Area of a circle $= \pi r^2$

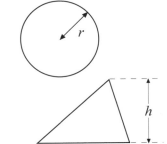

Area of a triangle $= \dfrac{1}{2} b h$

(h is perpendicular height)

Area of a parallelogram $= b h$

Example 1

Calculate the *area* of the triangle shown.

Solution

Area $= \dfrac{1}{2} \times 4 \times 6$

$= 12 \ \text{cm}^2$

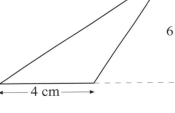

6 cm

4 cm

Example 2

Calculate the *area of* a circle with diameter 10 m.

Solution

Radius $= 10 \div 2 = 5$ m

Area $= \pi \times 5^2 = 78.53981634 \ \text{m}^2$

$= 78.5 \ \text{m}^2$ (to 3 significant figures)

Example 3

Calculate the *area* of the shape shown:

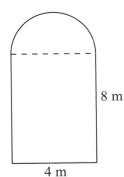

8 m

4 m

Solution

Area of rectangle $= 4 \times 8$

$\qquad\qquad\qquad = 32 \text{ m}^2$

Radius of semicircle $= 4 \div 2 = 2 \text{ m}$

Area of semicircle $= \dfrac{1}{2} \times \pi \times 2^2$

$\qquad\qquad\qquad = 6.283185307 \text{ m}^2$

Total area $= 32 + 6.283185307 = 38.283185307 \text{ m}^2$

$\qquad\qquad\quad = 38.3 \text{ m}^2$ (to 3 significant figures)

Example 4

The diagram shows a piece of card in the shape of a parallelogram, that has had a circular hole cut in it.

Calculate the area of the shaded part.

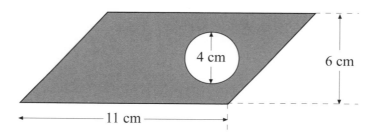

Solution

Area of parallelogram $= 11 \times 6$

$\qquad\qquad\qquad\quad = 66 \text{ cm}^2$

Radius of circle $= 4 \div 2 = 2 \text{ cm}$

Area of circle $= \pi \times 2^2$

$\qquad\qquad\quad = 12.56637061 \text{ cm}^2$

Area of shape $= 66 - 12.56637061 = 53.43362939 \text{ cm}^2$

$\qquad\qquad\quad = 53.4 \text{ cm}^2$ (to 3 significant figures)

Exercises

1. Calculate the area of each of the following shapes:

    (a)
    (b)

    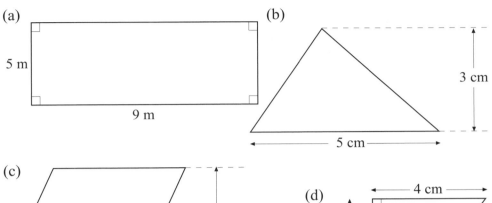

    (c)
    (d)

    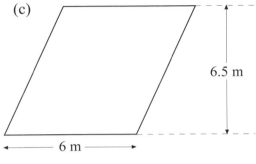
    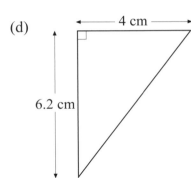

2. Calculate, giving your answers correct to 3 significant figures, the *area* of a circle with:

    (a) radius 6 m,   (b) diameter 20 cm,   (c) diameter 9 cm.

3. Calculate the *area* of each of the following shapes, giving your answers correct to 3 significant figures:

    (a)   (b)

    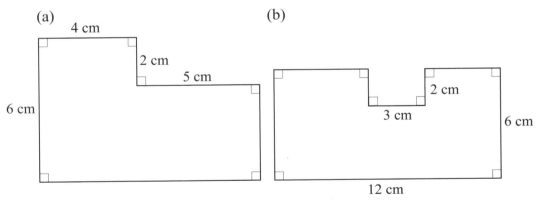

    (c)   (d)

    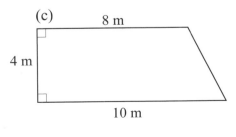
    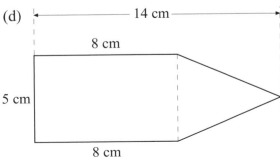

4.   Calculate, giving your answers correct to 3 significant figures, the *area* of
      the semicircle with:

      (a)   radius 30 cm,   (b)   diameter 14 mm.

5.   A circle of radius 8 cm is cut into 6 parts
      of equal size, as shown in the diagram.

      Calculate the *area* of each part, giving
      your answer correct to 2 decimal places.

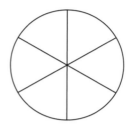

6.   Giving your answers correct to 3 significant figures, calculate the *area* of
      each of the following shapes. Each of the curved parts is a semicircle.

      (a)   (b)

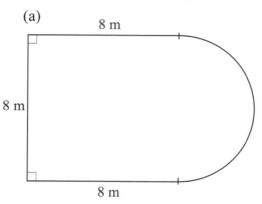

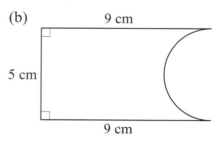

      (c)   (d)

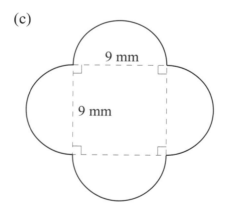

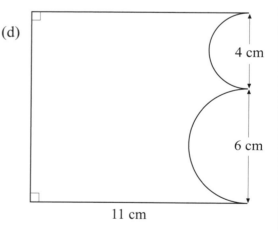

7.   A rectangular metal plate is shown in
      the diagram. Four holes of diameter
      8 mm are drilled in the plate.

      Calculate the *area* of the remaining
      metal, giving your answer correct
      to 2 decimal places.

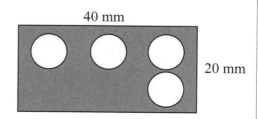

8. Calculate the *area* of the shape shown, giving your answer correct to 1 decimal place.

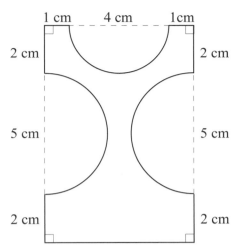

9. The area that has been shaded in the diagram has an area of 21.8 cm^2. Calculate the *diameter* of the semi-circular hole, giving your answer to the nearest millimetre.

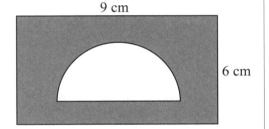

10. The diagram shows the lid of a child's shape-sorter box. Calculate the *area* of the lid, giving your answer correct to 1 decimal place.

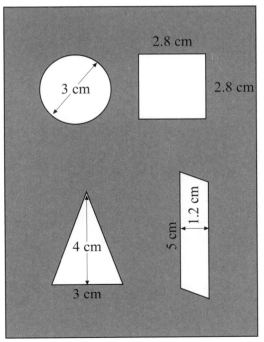

11.   Each shape in this question has an *area* of 10 cm^2.
      No diagram is drawn to scale.

      (a)   Calculate the height of the parallelogram.

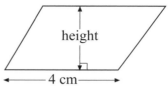

      (b)   Calculate the length of the base of the
            triangle.

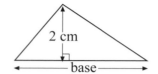

      (c)   What might be the values of *h, a* and *b*
            in this trapezium?

            What else might be the values of
            h, a and *b* ?

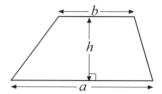

      (d)   Look at this rectangle:

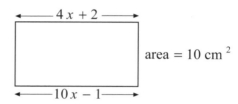

            Calculate the value of *x* and use it to find the length and width of
            the rectangle.
            Show your working.

                                                        (KS3/98/Ma/Tier 5-7/P1)

12.   This shape is designed using 3 semi-circles.

      The radii of the semi-circles are 3*a*, 2*a* and *a*.

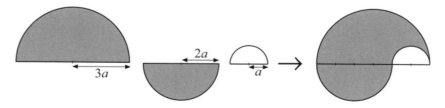

      (a)   Find the area of each semi-circle, in terms of *a* and π, and show that
            the *total* area of the shape is $6\pi a^2$.

      (b)   The area, $6\pi a^2$, of the shape is 12 cm^2.

            Write an equation in the form *a* = ... , leaving your answer in
            terms of π.

            Show your working and *simplify* your equation.

                                                        (KS3/98/Ma/Tier 6-8/P1)

13. Calculate the area of this triangle.

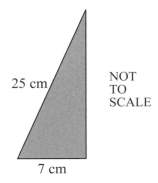

25 cm

NOT
TO
SCALE

7 cm

Show your working.

(KS3/97/Ma/Tier 5-7/P2)

14. A box for coffee is in the shape of a hexagonal prism.

One end of the box is shown below.

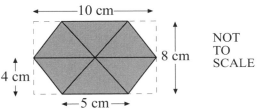

NOT
TO
SCALE

Each of the 6 triangles in the hexagon has the same dimensions.

(a) Calculate the total *area* of the hexagon.
Show your working.

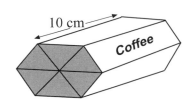

(b) The box is 10 cm long.

After packing, the coffee fills 80%
of the box.

How many grams of coffee are in the box?

(The mass of 1 cm^3 of coffee is 0.5 grams.)
Show your working.

(c) A 227 g packet of the same coffee costs £2.19.
How much per 100 g of coffee is this?
Show your working

(KS3/98/Ma/Tier 5-7/P2)

9.3 Perimeter of Special Shapes

In this section we calculate the perimeters of various shapes. The perimeter of a circle is referred to as the 'circumference'.

> The circumference, C, of a circle $= 2\pi r$ or πd where r is the radius and d is the diameter of the circle.

Example 1

Calculate the circumference of a circle with radius 8 cm.

Solution

Using the formula, $C = 2\pi r$, gives

$C = 2 \times \pi \times 8 = 50.26548246$ cm

$= 50.3$ cm (to 3 significant figures)

Example 2

The diagram shows a semicircle of diameter 12 cm.
Calculate the perimeter of the semicircle.

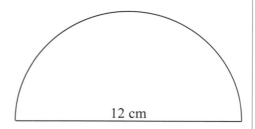

12 cm

Solution

Length of curve $= \pi \times 12 \div 2$

$\qquad = 18.84955592$ cm

Straight edge $= 12$ cm

Total perimeter $= 12 + 18.84955592$

$\qquad = 30.84955592$ cm

$\qquad = 30.8$ cm (to 3 significant figures.)

Example 3

The diagram shows a shape that is made up of a rectangle, a triangle and a semicircle.
Calculate its perimeter.

Solution

Length of curve $= \pi \times 7 \div 2$

$\qquad = 10.99557429$ cm

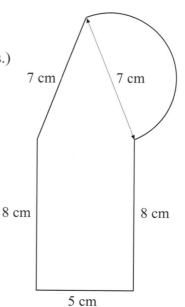

7 cm   7 cm

8 cm   8 cm

5 cm

Total perimeter $= 8 + 5 + 8 + 7 + 10.99557429$

$= 38.99557429$ cm

$= 39.0$ cm (to 3 significant figures)

Exercises

1. Giving your answers correct to 3 significant figures, calculate the *circumference* of a circle with:

    (a) radius 6 m, (b) diameter 15 cm, (c) radius 8 mm.

2. Calculate the *perimeter* of each of the following shapes:

    (a)

    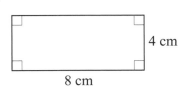

    4 cm

    8 cm

    (b)

    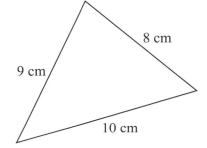

    8 cm

    9 cm

    10 cm

    (c)

    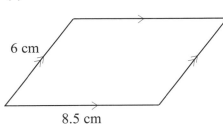

    6 cm

    8.5 cm

    (d)

    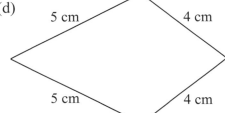

    5 cm   4 cm

    5 cm   4 cm

3. Giving your answer correct to 3 significant figures, calculate the *perimeter* of the semicircle shown.

    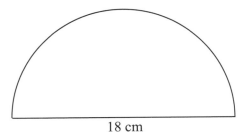

    18 cm

13

4.   A circle of radius 8 cm is cut into four
      equal parts as shown in the diagram:

      (a)   Calculate the *circumference* of the
             original circle, giving your answer
             correct to 2 decimal places.

      (b)   Calculate the *perimeter* of each of
             the 4 parts, giving your answers
             correct to 2 decimal places.

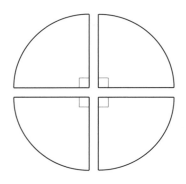

5.   Calculate the *perimeter* of each of the following shapes, giving your answers
      correct to 1 decimal place.   The circular parts are either semicircles or
      quarters of circles.

      (a)   (b)

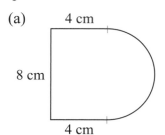

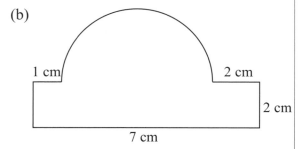

      (c)   (d)

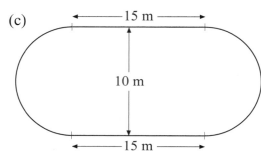

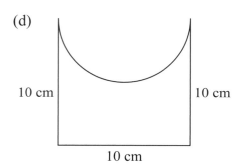

6.   Calculate the *perimeter* of each of the following shapes:

      (a)   (b)

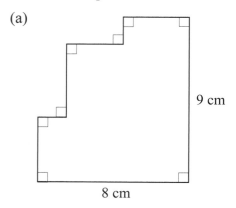

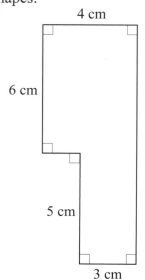

7. A square has an area of 36 m^2. Calculate its *perimeter.*

8. Calculate the *perimeter* of this shape, giving your answer correct to the nearest centimetre:

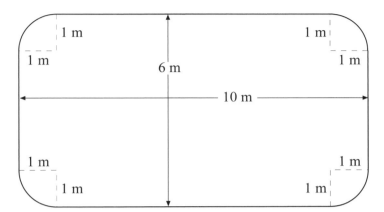

9. A circle of radius 32 cm is cut into 8 equal parts, as shown in the diagram.

   Calculate the *perimeter* of each part, giving your answer correct to the nearest millimetre.

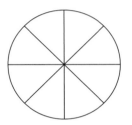

10. The total perimeter of a semicircle is 37 cm. Calculate the *radius* of the semicircle, giving your answer correct to the nearest millimetre.

11.   The perimeter of this shape is $3t + 2s$.

   $$p = 3t + 2s$$

   Write an expression for the perimeters of each of these shapes.
   Write each expression in its simplest form.

   (a)

   (b)

   (c)

   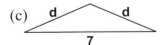

   (d)

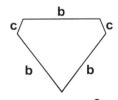

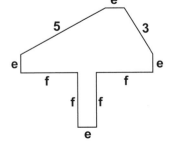

(KS3/95/Ma/3-5/P1)

12.   Each side of this hexagon is 1 cm long.

(a)   The shaded shape below is made from 7 hexagon tiles.
       Write down the perimeter of the shaded shape.

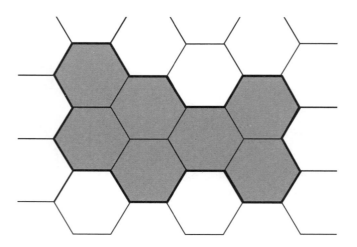

(b)   On a copy of the following diagram, shade a shape made with 7 tiles
       which has a *smaller* perimeter.

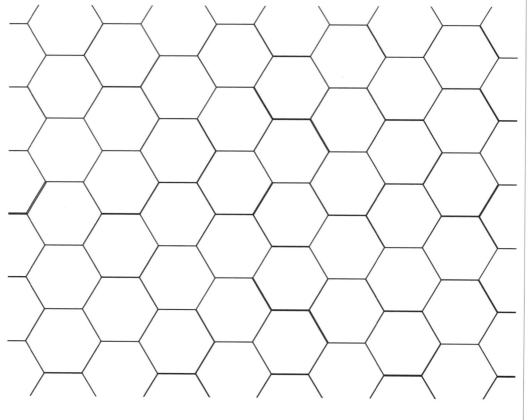

(c)   Explain what made its perimeter less than the perimeter of the first shape.

(d)   On a copy of the following diagram, shade a shape made with 7 tiles which has the *biggest* possible perimeter.

(e)   Explain what made your shape have the biggest possible perimeter.

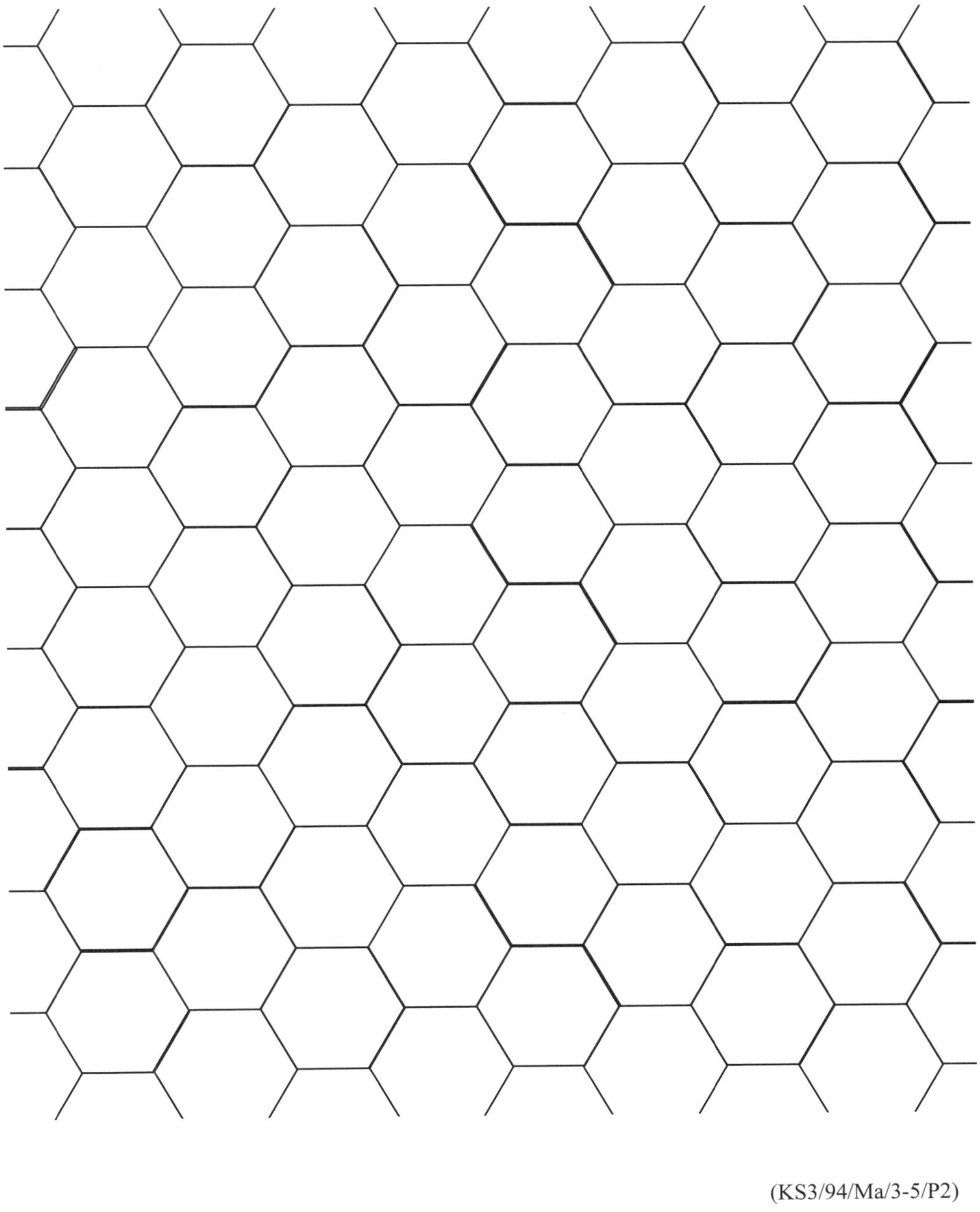

(KS3/94/Ma/3-5/P2)

13. Wyn and Jay are using their wheelchairs to measure distances.

    (a) The large wheel on Wyn's wheelchair has a diameter of 60 cm.
        Wyn pushes the wheel round exactly once.
        Calculate how far Wyn has moved.
        Show your working.

    (b) The large wheel on Jay's wheelchair has a diameter of 52 cm.
        Jay moves her wheelchair forward 950 cm.
        Calculate how many times the large wheel goes round.
        Show your working.

                                                        (KS3/96/Ma/Tier 5-7/P2)

14. (a) A circle has a radius of 15 cm.
        Calculate the *area* of the circle.
        Show your working.

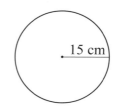

    (b) A different circle has a *circumference* of 120 cm.
        What is the radius of the circle?
        Show your working.

                                                        (KS3/99/Ma/Tier 5-7/P2)

9.4 Surface Area and Volume of 3-D Shapes

In this section we calculate the volume and surface area of 3-D shapes such as *cubes, cuboids, prisms* and *cylinders*.

Cube	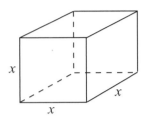	Volume $= x^3$ Surface area $= 6x^2$
Cuboid	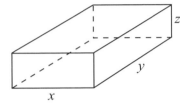	Volume $= xyz$ Surface area $= 2xy + 2xz + 2yz$
Cylinder	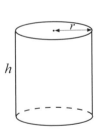	Volume $= \pi r^2 h$ Area of curved surface $= 2\pi rh$ Area of each end $= \pi r^2$ Total surface area $= 2\pi rh + 2\pi r^2$
Prism	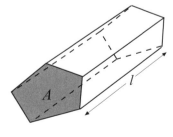	A prism has a uniform cross-section Volume $=$ area of cross-section $\times$ length $= Al$

Example 1

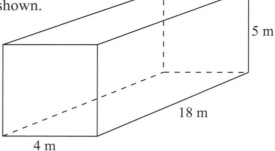

(a)   Calculate the *volume* of the cuboid shown.

(b)   Calculate the *surface area* of the cuboid shown.

Solution

(a)   Volume $= 4 \times 18 \times 5$

                $= 360 \text{ m}^3$

(b)   Surface area $= (2 \times 4 \times 18) + (2 \times 4 \times 5) + (2 \times 5 \times 18)$

                        $= 144 + 40 + 180$

                        $= 364 \text{ m}^2$

Example 2

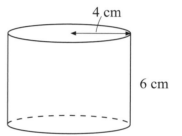

Calculate the *volume* and total *surface area* of the cylinder shown.

Solution

Volume $= \pi r^2 h = \pi \times 4^2 \times 6 = 96\pi$

           $= 301.5928947 \text{ cm}^3$

           $= 302 \text{ cm}^3$ (to 3 significant figures)

Area of curved surface $= 2\pi r h = 2 \times \pi \times 4 \times 6$

                          $= 48\pi$

                          $= 150.7964474 \text{ cm}^2$

Area of each end $= \pi r^2 = \pi \times 4^2$

                    $= 16\pi$

                    $= 50.26548246 \text{ cm}^2$

Total surface area $= 150.7964474 + (2 \times 50.26548246)$

                     $= 251.3274123 \text{ cm}^2$

                     $= 251 \text{ cm}^2$ (to 3 significant figures)

Note: From the working we can see that the area of the curved surface is 48π, and that the area of each end is 16π. The total surface area is therefore

$$48\pi + (2 \times 16\pi) = 80\pi = 251.3274123 \text{ cm}^2$$

                            $= 251 \text{ cm}^2$ (to 3 significant figures)

Example 3

Calculate the *volume* of this prism.

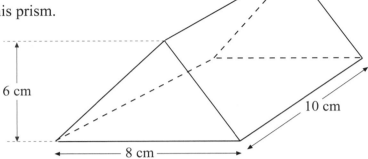

Solution

Area of end of prism $= \dfrac{1}{2} \times 8 \times 6$

$= 24 \text{ cm}^2$

Volume of prism $= 24 \times 10$

$= 240 \text{ cm}^3$

Exercises

1. Calculate the *volume* and *surface area* of each of the following cuboids:

    (a)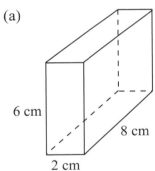

    (b)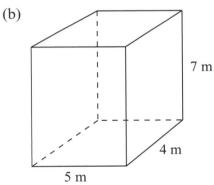

2. Giving your answers correct to 3 significant figures, calculate the *volume* and *total surface area* of each of the following cylinders:

    (a)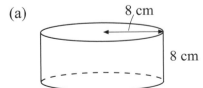

    (b)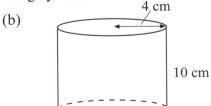

3.   Calculate the *volume* of each of the following prisms:

(a)   (b)

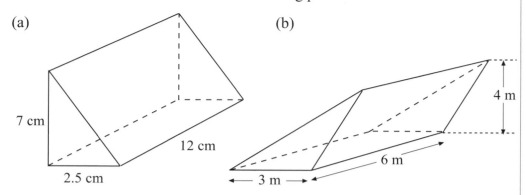

4.   Calculate the *volume* and *surface area* of the following prism:

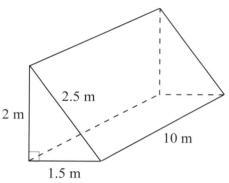

5.   The diagram shows a wooden block that has had a hole drilled in it. The diameter of the hole is 2 cm.

Calculate the *volume* of this solid, giving your answer correct to 2 decimal places.

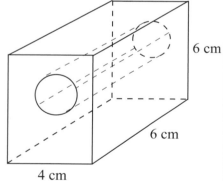

6.   A concrete beam is to rest on two concrete pillars. The beam is a cuboid with sides of length 0.5 m, 3 m and 0.4 m.

The pillars have diameter 0.4 m and height 2 m.

Calculate the *total volume* of concrete needed to make the beam and the pillars. Round your answer to a sensible level of accuracy.

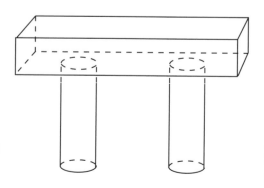

7. The diagram shows the cross-section of a pipe of length 50 cm.
The inner diameter of the pipe is 20 cm and the outer diameter is 30 cm.

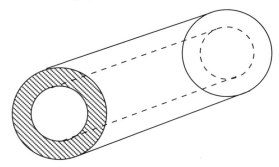

(a) Calculate the *volume* of metal needed to make the pipe. Round your answer to a sensible level of accuracy.

(b) Calculate the *total surface area* of the pipe, including the inside surface. Round your answer to a sensible level of accuracy.

8. The diagram shows a prism. The cross-section of the prism consists of a rectangle and a semicircle.

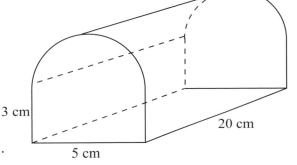

3 cm

5 cm

20 cm

(a) Calculate the *volume* of the prism. Give your answer to the nearest cm^3.

(b) Calculate the *total surface area* of the prism. Give your answer to the nearest cm^2.

9. The volume of the prism shown is 720 mm^3.

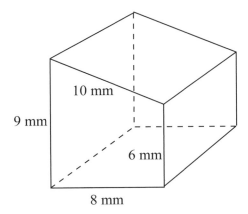

10 mm

9 mm

6 mm

8 mm

(a) Determine the *length* of the prism.

(b) Calculate the *surface area* of the prism.

10. A cylinder has a diameter of 12 cm and a curved surface area of 132π or 415 cm^2 (to 3 significant figures).

    (a) Determine the *height* of the cylinder.

    (b) Calculate the *volume* of the cylinder, giving your answer to the nearest cm^3.

11. (a) These cuboids are made from small cubes.
Write *how many small cubes* there are in each cuboid.
The first is done for you.

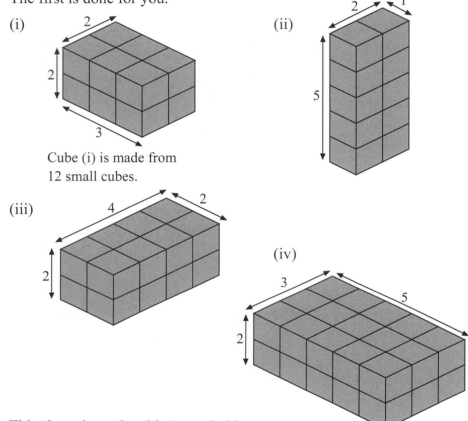

    (i)

    Cube (i) is made from 12 small cubes.

    (ii)

    (iii)

    (iv)

    (b) This shape is made with two cuboids.
Write *how many cubes* there are in this shape.

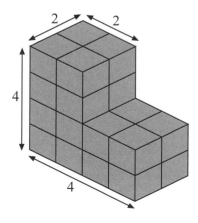

(KS3/98/Ma/Tier 3-5/P1)

12. (a) What is the volume of this *standard size* box of salt?

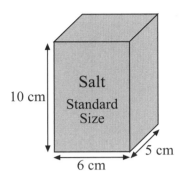

(b) What is the volume of this *special offer* box of salt, which is 20% bigger?

The standard size box contains enough salt to fill up 10 salt pots.

(c) How many salt pots may be filled up from the *special offer* box of salt?

(KS3/96/Ma/Tier 5-7/P2)

13. (a) Look at this triangle.

Show working to explain why angle *x must* be a right angle.

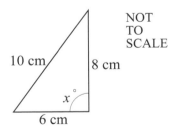

(b) What is the volume of this prism?

You *must* show *each step* in your working.

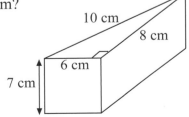

(c)   Prisms A and B have the same cross-sectional area.

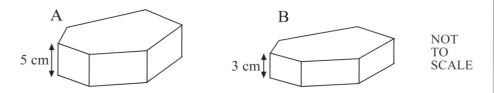

NOT
TO
SCALE

Copy and complete the table:

	Prism A	Prism B
height	5 cm	3 cm
volume	200 cm^3	.... cm^3

(KS3/99/Ma/Tier 5-7/P1)

14.   TJ's Cat Food is sold in tins shaped like this.
       Each tin has an internal height of 5 cm.

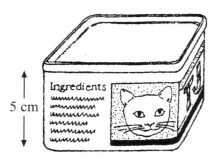

(a)   The area of the lid of the tin is 35 cm^2.
       Work out the volume of cat food that the tin contains.

(b)   The label that goes round the tin overlaps by 1 cm.

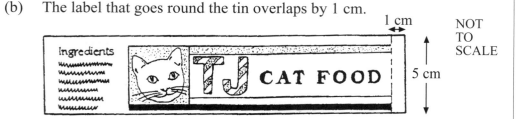

NOT
TO
SCALE

The area of the label is 134 cm^2.

Work out the distance around the tin.

Show your working.

TJ's Cat Food plans to use tins that are the shape of cylinders.

The internal measurements of a tin are shown.

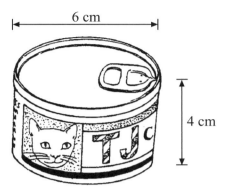

6 cm

4 cm

(c)   Work out the volume of cat food that the tin contains.
Show your working.

(KS3/95/Ma/Levels 5-7/P2)

10 Sequences

10.1 Constant Differences

In the first part of this unit we consider sequences where the difference between successive terms is the same every time. We also use formulae to create the terms of a sequence.

Example 1

Write down the next 3 terms of each of the following sequences:

(a)   7, 11, 15, 19, 23, ...

(b)   1, 9, 17, 25, 33, ...

Solution

(a)   7   11   15   19   23   ...

$$\vee \quad \vee \quad \vee \quad \vee$$

       4   4   4   4

The difference between each term and the next is always 4. This value is called the *first difference*. So we can continue the sequence by adding 4 each time. This gives the sequence:

7, 11, 15, 19, 23, 27, 31, 35

(b)   1   9   17   25   33   ...

$$\vee \quad \vee \quad \vee \quad \vee$$

       8   8   8   8

Here the difference between each term and the next is always 8. To continue the sequence we must keep on adding 8 every time. This gives the sequence:

1, 9, 17, 25, 33, 41, 49, 57

Example 2

A sequence is defined by the formula $u_n = 3n + 1$.

Calculate the first 5 terms of this sequence.

Solution

The first term, often called u_1, is formed by substituting $n = 1$ into the formula.

$$u_1 = 3 \times 1 + 1$$

$$= 3 + 1$$

$$= 4$$

For the second term, substitute $n = 2$ to give:

$$u_2 = 3 \times 2 + 1$$
$$= 7$$

For the third term, substitute $n = 3$ to give:

$$u_3 = 3 \times 3 + 1$$
$$= 10$$

For the fourth term, substitute $n = 4$ to give:

$$u_4 = 3 \times 4 + 1$$
$$= 13$$

For the fifth term, substitute $n = 5$ to give:

$$u_5 = 3 \times 5 + 1$$
$$= 16$$

So the first 5 terms of the sequence are

$$4, \quad 7, \quad 10, \quad 13, \quad 16.$$

Example 3

The terms of a sequence are given by the formula $u_n = 8n - 3$.

Calculate:

(a)   the first 3 terms of the sequence,

(b)   the 100th term of the sequence,

(c)   the 200th term of the sequence.

Solution

(a) $n = 1$ gives $u_1 = 8 \times 1 - 3$
$$= 5$$

$n = 2$ gives $u_2 = 8 \times 2 - 3$
$$= 13$$

$n = 3$ gives $u_3 = 8 \times 3 - 3$
$$= 21$$

So the first 3 terms are

$$5, \quad 13, \quad 21.$$

(b) $n = 100$ gives $u_{100} = 8 \times 100 - 3$

$$= 797$$

So the 100th term of the sequence is 797.

(c) $n = 200$ gives $u_{200} = 8 \times 200 - 3$

$$= 1597$$

So the 200th term of the sequence is 1597.

Exercises

1.   Write down the next 3 terms of each of the following sequences:

     (a)   2,   5,   8,   11,   14,   ...

     (b)   9,   18,   27,   36,   45,   ...

     (c)   13,   14,   15,   16,   17,   ...

     (d)   7,   15,   23,   31,   39,   ...

2.   Write down the next 3 terms of each of the following sequences:

     (a)   100,   98,   96,   94,   92,   ...

     b)   20,   17,   14,   11,   8,   ...

     (c)   48,   43,   38,   33,   28,   ...

     (d)   17,   13,   9,   5,   1,   ...

3.   A sequence is defined by the formula $u_n = 6n - 2$.

     (a)   Calculate the first 5 terms of the sequence.

     (b)   What is the difference between the terms of the sequence?

4.   A sequence is defined by the formula $u_n = 8n + 2$.

     (a)   Calculate the first 5 terms of the sequence.

     (b)   What is the difference between the terms of the sequence?

     (c)   Write down the next 3 terms of the sequence.

5.   A sequence is given by $u_n = 7n - 3$.

     (a)   Calculate the first 4 terms of the sequence.

     (b)   What is the difference between the terms of the sequence?

     (c)   Explain where the difference appears in the formula for the terms.

6. A sequence is given by $u_n = 9n + 2$.

   (a) Calculate the first 4 terms of the sequence.

   (b) How does the difference between terms relate to the formula?

7. A sequence is given by the formula $u_n = 11n - 7$.

   (a) What would you expect to be the difference between the terms of the sequence?

   (b) Calculate the first 4 terms of the sequence and check your answer to part (a).

   (c) Calculate the 10th term of the sequence.

8. A sequence is defined by the formula $u_n = 82 - 4n$.

   (a) Calculate the first 5 terms of the sequence.

   (b) What is the difference between terms for the sequence?

   (c) How does this difference relate to the formula?

   (d) Calculate the 20th term of the sequence.

9. (a) Calculate the 100th term of the sequence given by $u_n = 8n - 5$.

   (b) Calculate the 25th term of the sequence given by $u_n = 11n - 3$.

   (c) Calculate the 200th term of the sequence given by $u_n = 3n + 22$.

   (d) Calculate the 58th term of the sequence defined by $u_n = 1000 - 5n$.

10. Four sequences, A, B, C and D, are defined by the following formulae:

      A $u_n = 8n + 2$

      B $u_n = 7n - 3$

      C $u_n = 3n + 1$

      D $u_n = 100 - 6n$

   (a) Which sequences have 4 as their first term?

   (b) Which sequence is *decreasing*?

   (c) Which sequence has a difference of 7 between terms?

   (d) Which sequence has 301 as its 100th term?

11. (a) Look at this part of a number line.
    Write down the 2 missing numbers.

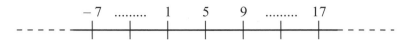

$$-7 \quad \ldots\ldots \quad 1 \quad 5 \quad 9 \quad \ldots\ldots \quad 17$$

Copy and complete this sentence:

The numbers on this line go *up* in steps of ....

(b) This is a *different* number line.
    Write down the 3 missing numbers.

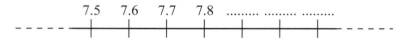

$$7.5 \quad 7.6 \quad 7.7 \quad 7.8 \quad \ldots\ldots \quad \ldots\ldots \quad \ldots\ldots$$

Copy and complete this sentence:

The numbers on this line go *up* in steps of ....

(KS3/97/Ma/Tier 4-6/P1)

12. Jeff makes a sequence of patterns with black and grey triangular tiles.

pattern number 1   pattern number 2   pattern number 3

The rule for finding the number of tiles in pattern number N in Jeff's sequence is:

$$\boxed{\text{number of tiles} = 1 + 3\,N}$$

(a) The 1 in this rule represents the *black tile.*
    What does the 3N represent?

(b) Jeff makes *pattern number 12* in his sequence.
    How many *black* tiles and how many *grey* tiles does he use?

(c) Jeff uses 61 tiles altogether to make a pattern in his sequence.
    What is the number of the pattern he makes?

(d)   Barbara makes a sequence of patterns with *hexagonal* tiles.

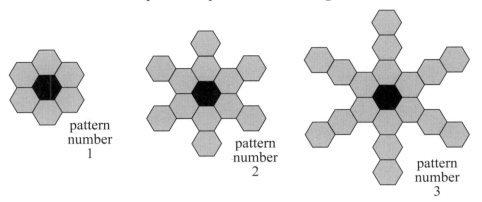

Each pattern in Barbara's sequence has 1 black tile in the middle.

Each new pattern has 6 more grey tiles than the pattern before.

Copy and complete the rule for finding the number of tiles in pattern number N in Barbara's sequence.

number of tiles = ... + ...

(e)   Gwenno uses some tiles to make a *different* sequence of patterns.

The rule for finding the number of tiles in pattern number N in Gwenno's sequence is:

number of tiles $= 1 + 4N$

Draw what you think the first 3 patterns in Gwenno's sequence could be.

(KS3/99/Ma/Tier 5-7/P2)

13.   Owen has some tiles like these:

He uses the tiles to make a series of patterns.

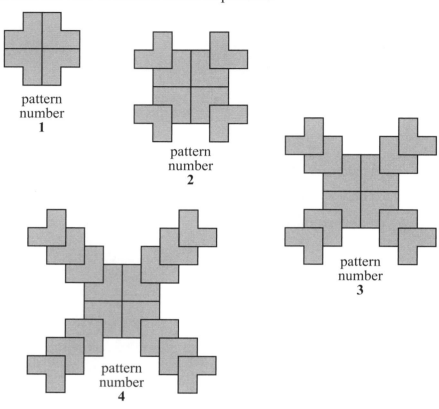

(a)   Each new pattern has *more tiles* than the one before.
The number of tiles goes up by the same amount each time.

How many *more* tiles does Owen add each time he makes a new pattern?

(b)   *How many tiles* will Owen need altogether to make *pattern number* 6 ?

(c)   *How many tiles* will Owen need altogether to make *pattern number* 9 ?

(d)   Owen uses 40 tiles to make a pattern.

What is the number of the pattern he makes?

(KS3/98/Ma/Tier 4-6/P2)

10.2 Finding the Formula for a Linear Sequence

It is possible to determine a formula for linear sequences, i.e. sequences where the difference between successive terms is always the same.

The first differences for the number pattern

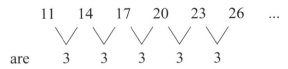

are   11   14   17   20   23   26   ...
         3   3   3   3   3

If we look at the sequence $3n$, i.e. the multiples of 3, and compare it with our original sequence

our sequence	11	14	17	20	23	26
sequence $3n$	3	6	9	12	15	18

we can see easily that the formula that generates our number pattern is

nth term of sequence $= 3n + 8$

i.e. $u_n = 3n + 8$

If, however, we had started with the sequence

38   41   44   47   50   53   ...

the first differences would still have been 3 and the comparison of this sequence with the sequence $3n$

our sequence	38	41	44	47	50	53
sequence $3n$	3	6	9	12	15	18

would have led to the formula $u_n = 3n + 35$.

In the same way, the sequence

-7 -4 -1 2   5   8   ...

also has first differences 3 and the comparison

our sequence	-7	-4	-1	2	5	8
sequence $3n$	3	6	9	12	15	18

yields the formula $u_n = 3n - 10$.

From these examples, we can see that any sequence with constant first difference 3 has the formula

$u_n = 3n + c$

where the adjustment constant c may be either positive or negative.

This approach can be applied to any linear sequence, giving us the general rule that:

> If the *first* difference between *successive* terms is d, then
>
> $$u_n = d \times n + c$$

Example 1

Determine a formula for this sequence:

7, 13, 19, 25, 31, ...

Solution

First consider the differences between the terms,

$$
\begin{array}{ccccc}
7 & 13 & 19 & 25 & 31 & \ldots \\
\end{array}
$$

$$
\begin{array}{cccc}
6 & 6 & 6 & 6
\end{array}
$$

As the difference is always 6, we can write,

$$u_n = 6n + c$$

As the first term is 7, we can write down the equation:

$$
\begin{aligned}
7 &= 6 \times 1 + c \\
&= 6 + c \\
c &= 1
\end{aligned}
$$

So the formula will be,

$$u_n = 6n + 1$$

We can check that this formula is correct by testing it on other terms, for example,

the 4th term $= 6 \times 4 + 1 = 25$

which is correct.

Example 2

Determine a formula for this sequence:

2, 7, 12, 17, 22, 27, ...

Solution

First consider the differences between the terms,

$$
\begin{array}{cccccc}
2 & 7 & 12 & 17 & 22 & 27 & \ldots \\
\end{array}
$$

$$
\begin{array}{ccccc}
5 & 5 & 5 & 5 & 5
\end{array}
$$

The difference between each term is always 5, so the formula will be,

$$u_n = 5n + c$$

The first term can be used to form an equation to determine c:

$$2 = 5 \times 1 + c$$

$$2 = 5 + c$$

$$c = -3$$

So the formula will be,

$$u_n = 5n - 3$$

> Note that the constant term, c, is given by
>
> $c = $ first term $-$ first difference

Example 3

Determine a formula for the sequence:

28, 25, 22, 19, 16, 13, ...

Solution

First consider the differences between the terms,

28   25   22   19   16   13   ...

-3 -3 -3 -3 -3

Here the difference is *negative* because the terms are becoming smaller.

Using the difference as -3 gives,

$$u_n = -3n + c$$

The first term is 28, so

$$28 = -3 \times 1 + c$$

$$28 = -3 + c$$

$$c = 31$$

The general formula is then,

$$u_n = -3n + 31$$

or

$$u_n = 31 - 3n$$

Exercises

1.   For the sequence,

          7, 11, 15, 19, ...

      (a)   calculate the *difference* between successive terms,

      (b)   determine the *formula* that generates the sequence.

2.   Determine the *formula* for each of the following sequences:

      (a)   6, 10, 14, 18, 22, ...

      (b)   11, 13, 15, 17, 19, ...

      (c)   9, 16, 23, 30, 37, ...

      (d)   34, 56, 78, 100, 122, ...

      (e)   22, 31, 40, 49, 58, ...

3.   One number is missing from the following sequence:

          1, 6, 11, ☐ , 21, 26, 31

      (a)   What is the missing number?

      (b)   Calculate the *difference* between successive terms.

      (c)   Determine the *formula* that generates the sequence.

4.   Determine the *general formula* for each of the following sequences:

      (a)   1, 4, 7, 10, 13, ...   (b)   2, 6, 10, 14, 18, ...

      (c)   4, 13, 22, 31, 40, ...   (d)   5, 15, 25, 35, 45, ...

      (e)   1, 20, 39, 58, 77, ...

5.   For the sequence,

          18, 16, 14, 12, 10, ...

      (a)   calculate the *difference* between successive terms,

      (b)   determine the *formula* that generates the sequence.

6.   Determine the *general formula* for each of the following sequences:

      (a)   19, 16, 13, 10, 7, ...   (b)   100, 96, 92, 88, 84, ...

      (c)   41, 34, 27, 20, 13, ...   (d)   66, 50, 34, 18, 2, ...

      (e)   90, 81, 72, 63, 54, ...

7.   For the sequence,

$$-2, \ -4, \ -6, \ -8, \ -10, \ -12, \ ...$$

(a)   calculate the *difference* between successive terms,

(b)   determine the *formula* for the sequence.

8.   Determine the *formula* that generates each of the following sequences:

(a) $0, \ -5, \ -10, \ -15, \ -20, \ ...$

(b) $-18, \ -16, \ -14, \ -12, \ -10, \ ...$

(c) $-5, \ -8, \ -11, \ -14, \ -17, \ ...$

(d) $8, \ 1, \ -6, \ -13, \ -20, \ ...$

(e) $-7, \ -3, \ 1, \ 5, \ 9, \ ...$

9.   A sequence has first term 20 and the difference between the terms is always 31.

(a)   Determine a *formula* to generate the terms of the sequence.

(b)   Calculate the *first 5 terms* of the sequence.

10.   The second and third terms of a sequence are 16 and 27. The difference between successive terms in the sequence is always constant.

(a)   Determine the *general formula* for the sequence.

(b)   Calculate the *first 5 terms* of the sequence.

11.   This is a series of patterns with grey and white tiles.

pattern
number
1

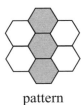

pattern
number
2

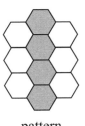

pattern
number
3

The series of patterns continues by adding each time.

(a)   Copy and complete this table:

pattern number	number of grey tiles	number of white tiles
5		
16		

(b)   Copy and complete this table by writing *expressions*:

pattern number	expression for the number of *grey* tiles	expression for the number of *white* tiles
n		

(c)   Write an expression to show the *total* number of tiles in pattern number n. Simplify your expression.

(d)   A different series of patterns is made with tiles.

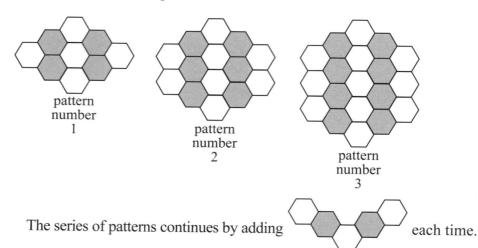

pattern number 1

pattern number 2

pattern number 3

The series of patterns continues by adding ⬡⬡⬡ each time.

For this series of patterns, write an expression to show the *total* number of tiles in pattern number n.

Show your working and *simplify* your expression.

(KS3/98/Ma/Tier 5-7/P1)

10.3   Second Differences and Quadratic Sequences

In section 10.2 we dealt with sequences where the differences between the terms was a constant value. In this section we extend this idea to sequences where the differences are *not constant*.

Example 1

(a)   Calculate the first 6 terms of the sequence defined by the quadratic formula,

$$u_n = n^2 + n - 1$$

(b)   Calculate the first differences between the terms.

(c)   Comment on the results you obtain.

Solution

(a)　Substituting $n = 1$ gives,

$$u_1 = 1^2 + 1 - 1$$
$$= 1$$

For $n = 2$,
$$u_2 = 2^2 + 2 - 1$$
$$= 5$$

For $n = 3$,
$$u_3 = 3^2 + 3 - 1$$
$$= 11$$

For $n = 4$,
$$u_4 = 4^2 + 4 - 1$$
$$= 19$$

For $n = 5$,
$$u_5 = 5^2 + 5 - 1$$
$$= 29$$

For $n = 6$,
$$u_6 = 6^2 + 6 - 1$$
$$= 41$$

So the first 6 terms are,

1,　5,　11,　19,　29,　41

(b)　The differences can now be calculated,

(c)　Note that the differences between the first differences are constant. They are all equal to 2. These are called the *second differences*, as shown below.

Sequence　　　　1　5　11　19　29　41

First differences　　4　6　8　10　12

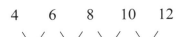

Second differences　　2　2　2　2

Example 2

(a)   Calculate the first 5 terms of the sequence defined by the quadratic formula

$$u_n = 3n^2 - n - 2$$

(b)   Determine the first and second differences for this sequence.

(c)   Comment on your results.

Solution

(a)   For $n = 1$, $u_1 = 3 \times 1^2 - 1 - 2$

$$= 3 - 1 - 2$$

$$= 0$$

For $n = 2$, $u_2 = 3 \times 2^2 - 2 - 2$

$$= 8$$

For $n = 3$, $u_3 = 3 \times 3^2 - 3 - 2$

$$= 22$$

For $n = 4$, $u_4 = 3 \times 4^2 - 4 - 2$

$$= 42$$

For $n = 5$, $u_5 = 3 \times 5^2 - 5 - 2$

$$= 68$$

So the sequence is,

$$0, \quad 8, \quad 22, \quad 42, \quad 68, \quad ...$$

(b)   The differences are calculated below:

Sequence	0		8		22		42		68	...
First differences		8		14		20		26		
Second differences			6		6		6			

(c)   Again, the second differences are constant; this time they are all 6.

Note

For a sequence defined by a *quadratic formula,* the second differences will be constant and equal to twice the number of n^2.

For example,

$$u_n = n^2 + n - 1 \qquad \text{Second difference} = 2$$

$$u_n = 3n^2 - n - 2 \qquad \text{Second difference} = 6$$

$$u_n = 5n^2 - n + 7 \qquad \text{Second difference} = 10$$

Example 3

Determine a formula for the general term of the sequence,

2, 9, 20, 35, 54, ...

Solution

Consider the first and second differences of the sequence:

2   9   20   35   54   ...

7   11   15   19

4   4   4

As the second differences are constant and equal to 4, the formula will begin

$$u_n = 2n^2 + ...$$

To determine the rest of the formula, subtract $2n^2$ from each term of the sequence, as shown below:

Sequence	2	9	20	35	54	...
$2n^2$	2	8	18	32	50	
New sequence	0	1	2	3	4	

1   1   1   1

The new sequence has a constant difference of 1 and begins with 0, so for this sequence the formula is $n - 1$.

Combining this with the $2n^2$ gives

$$u_n = 2n^2 + n - 1$$

Example 4

(a)   Calculate the first and second differences for the sequence,
        4, 1, 0, 1, 4, 9, ...

(b)   Use the differences to determine the next 2 terms of the sequence.

(c)   Determine a formula for the general term of the sequence.

Solution

(a)

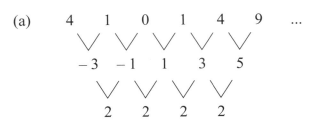

(b)   Extending the sequences above gives,

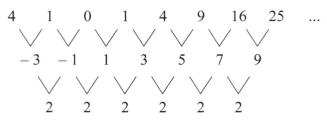

(c)   As the second differences are constant and all equal to 2, the formula will contain an 'n^2' term, and be of the form

$$u_n = n^2 + an + b$$

We must now determine the values of a and b. The easiest way to do this is to subtract n^2 from each term of the sequence, to form a new, simpler sequence.

our sequence	4	1	0	1	4	9
sequence n^2	1	4	9	16	25	36
new sequence	3	-3	-9	-15	-21	-27

The new sequence

$$
\begin{array}{ccccccc}
3 & -3 & -9 & -15 & -21 & -27 & \dots \\
& -6 & -6 & -6 & -6 & -6 &
\end{array}
$$

has constant first differences of -6 so will be given by $-6n + b$.

Using the first term gives,

$$3 = -6 \times 1 + b$$
$$b = 9$$

Thus the formula for the simpler sequence is $-6n + 9$.

Now combining this with the n^2 term gives,

$$u_n = n^2 - 6n + 9$$

Exercises

1. (a) Calculate the first 6 terms of the sequence defined by,

    $$u_n = n^2 + 2n + 1$$

    (b) Calculate the second differences for the sequence.

    (c) Use the differences to calculate the next 2 terms of the sequence.

2. A sequence has its general term defined as,

    $$u_n = 8n^2 - n - 1$$

    (a) What would you expect to be the second differences for the sequence?

    (b) Calculate the first 5 terms of the sequence.

    (c) Calculate the second differences for the sequence. Did you obtain the values you expected?

3. A sequence is listed below:

    6, 9, 14, 21, 30, 41, ...

    (a) Calculate the second differences for the sequence.

    (b) Determine the formula for the general term of the sequence.

4. Determine the formula for the general term of each of the following sequences:

    (a) 1, 7, 17, 31, 49, 71, ...

    (b) 6, 18, 38, 66, 102, 146, ...

    (c) − 5, 10, 35, 70, 115, 170, ...

    (d) 1, 10, 25, 46, 73, 106, ...

5. A sequence is listed below:

    2, 9, 20, 35, 54, 77, ...

    (a) Calculate the second differences for this sequence.

    (b) Form a simpler sequence by subtracting $2n^2$ from each term.

    (c) Determine a formula for the general term of the simpler sequence.

    (d) Determine a formula for the general term of the original sequence.

6. (a) Calculate the second differences of the sequence,

    6, 17, 36, 63, 98, 141, ...

    (b) Determine the formula for the general term of the sequence.

7. Determine the formula for the general term of each of the following sequences:

    (a)   3, 17, 39, 69, 107, ...

    (b)   5, 18, 37, 62, 93, ...

    (c)   9, 23, 45, 75, 113, ...

    (d)   − 4, 12, 38, 74, 120, ...

8. (a)   Calculate the second differences for the sequence,

         9, 4, − 5, − 18, − 35, ...

    (b)   Determine the formula for the general term of the sequence.

    (c)   Hence show that the 20th term of the sequence is −770.

9. Determine the formula for the general term of the sequence,

         6, 10, 12, 12, 10, 6, ...

10. (a)   Calculate the first, second and third differences for the sequence,

         6, 13, 32, 69, 130, 221, ...

    (b)   Determine a formula for the general term of the sequence.

11. This is a series of patterns with grey and black tiles.

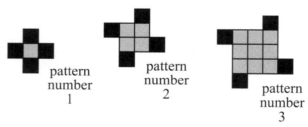

pattern number 1   pattern number 2   pattern number 3

    (a)   How many grey tiles and black tiles will there be in pattern number 8 ?

    (b)   How many grey tiles and black tiles will there be in pattern number 16 ?

    (c)   How many grey tiles and black tiles will there be in pattern number P ?

    (d)   T = total number of grey tiles and black tiles in a pattern
          P = pattern number

          Use symbols to write down an equation connecting T and P.

                                            (Ks3/96/Ma/Tier 6-8/P2)

10.4 Special Sequences

Before going on to look at harder examples, we list some of the important sequences that you should know:

1, 3, 5, 7, 9, 11, 13, ...
the *odd* numbers $\qquad u_n = 2n - 1$

2, 4, 6, 8, 10, 12, 14, ...
the *even* numbers $\qquad u_n = 2n$

1, 4, 9, 15, 25, 36, 49, ...
the *square* numbers $\qquad u_n = n^2$

1, 8, 27, 64, 125, 216, 343, ...
the *cube* numbers $\qquad u_n = n^3$

1, 3, 6, 10, 15, 21, 28, ...

the *triangular* numbers $\qquad u_n = \dfrac{1}{2}n(n + 1)$

There is one other important sequence, namely the *prime* numbers

2, 3, 5, 7, 11, 13, 17, 19, 23, 29, 31, ...

Note: there is no formula for calculating the *n*th prime number.

We now look at other, harder sequences generated by algebraic rules.

Example 1

(a) Write down the next 3 terms of the sequence,

1, 1, 2, 3, 5, 8, 13, ...

(b) Determine a formula for calculating the *n*th term.

Solution

(a) Use the first differences to extend the sequence:

1		1		2		3		5		8		13	...
	0		1		1		2		3		5		

Note that the first differences, ignoring the first 0, are in fact the actual sequence itself. These can then be used to extend the sequence:

1		1		2		3		5		8		13		21		34		55	...
	0		1		1		2		3		5		8		13		21		

47

(b)   Each term is the sum of the two previous terms; for example,

$$u_3 = u_2 + u_1$$

$$u_4 = u_3 + u_2$$

We can express this mathematically as,

$$u_n = u_{n-1} + u_{n-2}$$

This formula connects u_n to the two previous terms, rather than n which we used in the earlier sections. This sequence is actually a special sequence and is called the *Fibonacci* sequence.

Example 2

The first two terms of a sequence are 1 and 2. The sequence is defined as,

$$u_n = 2u_{n-1} + u_{n-2}$$

Calculate the next 3 terms of the sequence.

Solution

Note that $u_1 = 1$ and $u_2 = 2$.

$$
\begin{aligned}
u_3 &= 2u_2 + u_1 \\
    &= 2 \times 2 + 1 \\
    &= 5
\end{aligned}
$$

$$
\begin{aligned}
u_4 &= 2u_3 + u_2 \\
    &= 2 \times 5 + 2 \\
    &= 12
\end{aligned}
$$

$$
\begin{aligned}
u_5 &= 2u_4 + u_3 \\
    &= 2 \times 12 + 5 \\
    &= 29
\end{aligned}
$$

So the first 5 terms of the sequence are,

$$1, \ 2, \ 5, \ 12, \ 29$$

Example 3

For the sequence,

$$6, \ 12, \ 24, \ 48, \ 96, \ ...$$

(a)   calculate the next 2 terms of the sequence,

(b)   determine a general formula for the nth term.

Solution

(a)   Note that, in this sequence, each term is twice the previous term.

$$6 \quad 12 \quad 24 \quad 48 \quad 96 \quad 192 \quad 384 \quad ...$$
$$\times 2 \quad \times 2 \quad \times 2 \quad \times 2 \quad \times 2 \quad \times 2$$

(b)   Consider how each term is formed:

$$u_1 = 6 = 3 \times 2$$

$$u_2 = 12 = 3 \times 2 \times 2 = 3 \times 2^2$$

$$u_3 = 24 = 3 \times 2 \times 2 \times 2 = 3 \times 2^3$$

$$u_4 = 48 = 3 \times 2 \times 2 \times 2 \times 2 = 3 \times 2^4$$

Hence the general term will be $u_n = 3 \times 2^n$.

This sequence is an example of an *exponential* sequence.

Example 4

Consider the sequence,

$$\frac{3}{5}, \quad \frac{7}{8}, \quad \frac{11}{11}, \quad \frac{15}{14}, \quad \frac{19}{17}, \quad \frac{23}{20}, \quad ...$$

(a)   Write down the next 2 terms of the sequence,

(b)   Determine the general formula for the *n*th term of the sequence.

Solution

(a)   It is best to consider the numerators and the denominators separately.

First consider the sequence of numerators,

$$3 \quad 7 \quad 11 \quad 15 \quad 19 \quad 23 \quad ...$$
$$4 \quad 4 \quad 4 \quad 4 \quad 4$$

As the difference between the terms is 4, we have

$$u_n = 4n + a$$

and using the first term,

$$3 = 4 \times 1 + a$$

$$a = -1$$

Hence

$$u_n = 4n - 1$$

Now consider the sequence of denominators,

$$5 \quad 8 \quad 11 \quad 14 \quad 17 \quad 20 \quad ...$$

$$3 \quad 3 \quad 3 \quad 3 \quad 3$$

As the differences between terms is 3, we have

$$u_n = 3n + b$$

and, using the first term,

$$5 = 3 \times 1 + b$$
$$b = 2$$

Hence

$$u_n = 3n + 2$$

So for the given sequence of fractions we have,

$$u_n = \frac{4n - 1}{3n + 2}$$

Example 5

What happens to the sequence defined by,

$$u_n = \frac{n - 1}{n + 1}$$

as n becomes larger and larger?

Solution

The following table lists n and u_n for several values of n.

From the table it can be seen that the values of $u_n = \dfrac{n - 1}{n + 1}$ get larger and larger as n increases.

However, the numerator is always smaller than the denominator, so each value u_n must be smaller than 1.

It follows that, as n gets larger and larger, the values of u_n must get closer and closer to 1.

n	$u_n = \dfrac{n-1}{n+1}$	u_n to 3 decimal places
1	0	0
2	$\dfrac{1}{3}$	0.333
3	$\dfrac{2}{4}$	0.5
4	$\dfrac{3}{5}$	0.6
5	$\dfrac{4}{6}$	0.667
10	$\dfrac{9}{11}$	0.818
20	$\dfrac{19}{21}$	0.905
50	$\dfrac{49}{51}$	0.961
100	$\dfrac{99}{101}$	0.980
500	$\dfrac{499}{501}$	0.996
1000	$\dfrac{999}{1001}$	0.998
2000	$\dfrac{1999}{2001}$	0.999

Exercises

1. Calculate the next three terms in each of the following sequences:

   (a) 1, 3, 4, 7, 11, 18, ...

   (b) 4, 9, 13, 22, 35, ...

   (c) $\dfrac{1}{2}$, $\dfrac{2}{5}$, $\dfrac{3}{8}$, $\dfrac{4}{11}$, $\dfrac{5}{14}$, ...

   (d) 5, 15, 45, 135, 405, ...

2. Calculate the first 6 terms of each of the following sequences:

    (a) $u_1 = 0$, $u_2 = 3$, $u_n = u_{n-1} + u_{n-2}$

    (b) $u_1 = 3$, $u_2 = 4$, $u_n = 2u_{n-1} + u_{n-2}$

    (c) $u_1 = 6$, $u_2 = 10$, $u_n = 3u_{n-1} - u_{n-2}$

    (d) $u_1 = 1$, $u_2 = 2$, $u_n = u_{n-1} \times u_{n-2}$

3. (a) Calculate the next 3 terms of the sequence,

        1, 4, 16, 64, 256, ...

    (b) Determine a formula for the nth term of the sequence.

4. Determine the formula for the general term of each of the following sequences:

    (a) 15, 75, 375, 1875, 9375, ...

    (b) 1, 3, 9, 27, 81, ...

    (c) 20, 200, 2000, 20 000, 200 000, ...

    (d) 4, 28, 196, 1372, 9604, ...

5. (a) Determine the general formula for the terms of the sequence,

        1, 7, 13, 19, 25, 31, ...

    (b) Determine the general formula for the terms of the sequence,

        2, 10, 18, 26, 34, 42, ...

    (c) Determine the general formula for the terms of the sequence,

        $$\frac{1}{2}, \ \frac{7}{10}, \ \frac{13}{18}, \ \frac{19}{26}, \ \frac{25}{34}, \ \frac{31}{42}, \ \ ...$$

6. Determine the general formula for the terms of each of the following sequences:

    (a) $\dfrac{1}{4}, \ \dfrac{2}{5}, \ \dfrac{3}{6}, \ \dfrac{4}{7}, \ \dfrac{5}{8} \ \ ...$

    (b) $\dfrac{1}{3}, \ \dfrac{3}{11}, \ \dfrac{5}{19}, \ \dfrac{7}{27}, \ \dfrac{9}{35} \ \ ...$

    (c) $\dfrac{5}{7}, \ \dfrac{14}{12}, \ \dfrac{23}{17}, \ \dfrac{32}{22}, \ \dfrac{41}{27} \ \ ...$

    (d) $\dfrac{1}{10}, \ \dfrac{7}{20}, \ \dfrac{13}{40}, \ \dfrac{19}{80}, \ \dfrac{25}{160} \ \ ...$

7. Determine the formula for the general term of each of the following sequences, and also calculate the 10th term of each sequence.

   (a) $1, \dfrac{6}{7}, \dfrac{9}{11}, \dfrac{4}{5}, \dfrac{15}{19}, \ldots$

   (b) $\dfrac{1}{5}, \dfrac{3}{4}, 1, \dfrac{8}{7}, \dfrac{21}{17}, \ldots$

8. (a) Complete the following table for $u_n = \dfrac{2n}{n+1}$.

n	u_n	u_n to 3 decimal places
1		
5		
10		
50		
100		
500		
1000		
2000		

   (b) Describe what happens to u_n as n becomes larger and larger.

9. Complete tables similar to the one in question 8, for each of the following sequences:

   (a) $u_n = \dfrac{5n-1}{n}$

   (b) $u_n = \dfrac{6n+1}{n}$

   (c) $u_n = \dfrac{3n+1}{n+1}$

   (d) $u_n = \dfrac{n+1}{2n}$

   Comment on the results you obtain.

10. What do you think will happen to each of the sequences below as n becomes large?

   (a) $u_n = \dfrac{4n}{n+1}$

   (b) $u_n = \dfrac{7n+1}{n}$

   (c) $u_n = \dfrac{n}{2n+1}$

   (d) $u_n = \dfrac{4n}{2n-1}$

   Test your predictions with some larger and larger values of n .

11. (a) Here is a number chain:

$$2 \rightarrow 4 \rightarrow 6 \rightarrow 8 \rightarrow 10 \rightarrow 12 \rightarrow$$

The rule is: *add on 2 each time*

A *different* number chain is:

$$2 \rightarrow 4 \rightarrow 8 \rightarrow 16 \rightarrow 32 \rightarrow 64 \rightarrow$$

What could the rule be?

(b) Some number chains start like this:

$$1 \rightarrow 5 \rightarrow$$

Write down three *different* ways to continue this number chain.

For each chain write down the next three numbers.
Then write down the rule you are using.

(KS3/97/Ma/Tier 3-5/P2)

12. Each term of a number sequence is made by adding 1 to the numerator and 2 to the denominator of the previous term.

Here is the beginning of the number sequence:

$$\frac{1}{3}, \frac{2}{5}, \frac{3}{7}, \frac{4}{9}, \frac{5}{11}, \ldots$$

(a) Write an expression for the *n*th term of the sequence.

(b) The first five terms of the sequence are shown on the graph.

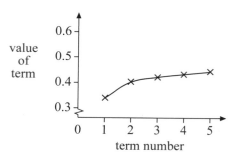

The sequence goes on and on for ever.

Which of the following four graphs shows how the sequence continues?

Graph 1   *Graph 2*

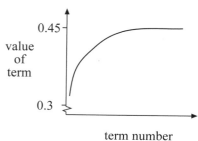   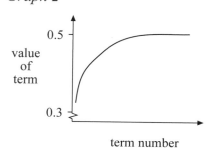

Graph 3

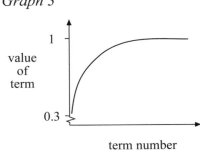

Graph 4

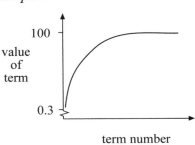

(c)   The *n*th term of a different sequence is $\dfrac{n}{n^2+1}$.

The *first term* of the sequence is $\dfrac{1}{2}$.

Write down the next *three terms*.

(d)   This new sequence also goes on and on for ever.

Which of the four graphs below shows how the sequence continues?

Graph 1

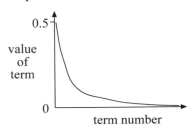

Graph 2

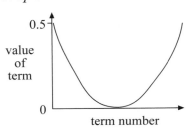

Graph 3

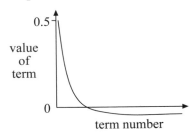

Graph 4

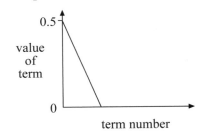

(KS3/99/Ma/Tier 6-8/P1)

55

11 | Algebraic Manipulation

11.1 | Equations, Formulae and Identities

In this section we discuss the difference between equations, formulae and identities, and then go on to make use of them.

An *equation* contains unknown quantities; for example,

$$3x + 2 = 11$$

This equation can be solved to determine x.

A *formula* links one quantity to one or more other quantities; for example,

$$A = \pi r^2$$

This formula can be used to determine A for any given value of r.

An *identity* is something that is always true for any values of the variables that are involved; for example,

$$2(x + y) \equiv 2x + 2y$$

and

$$(x + y)^2 \equiv x^2 + 2xy + y^2$$

If any pair of values of x and y are substituted, then the left hand side of an identity will generate the same value as the right hand side of that identity.

Example 1

The formula $C = \dfrac{5}{9}(F - 32)$ is used to convert temperatures in degrees Fahrenheit to degrees Celsius.

(a)   If $F = 41$, calculate C.

(b)   If $F = 131$, calculate C.

Solution

(a) $C = \dfrac{5}{9} \times (41 - 32)$

$C = \dfrac{5}{9} \times 9$

$C = 5$

(b) $C = \dfrac{5}{9} \times (131 - 32)$

$\quad C = \dfrac{5}{9} \times 99$

$\quad C = 55$

Example 2

A formula states that $v = u + at$.

Calculate v if $u = 10$, $a = 6.2$ and $t = 20$.

Solution

When substituting into equations, you need to be aware that the BODMAS rule applies automatically.

$v = u + at$

$v = 10 + 6.2 \times 20$

$v = 10 + 124$

$v = 134$

Example 3

Solve the following equations:

(a) $7x = 21$ (b) $x - 5 = 12$

(c) $2x + 1 = 6$ (d) $5x - 8 = 22$

Solution

(a) $7x = 21$

$\quad\quad x = \dfrac{21}{7}$ *Dividing both sides by 7*

$\quad\quad x = 3$

(b) $x - 5 = 12$

$\quad\quad\quad x = 12 + 5$ *Adding 5 to both sides*

$\quad\quad\quad x = 17$

(c) $2x + 1 = 6$

$\quad\quad\quad 2x = 6 - 1$ *Subtracting 1 from both sides*

$\quad\quad\quad 2x = 5$

$\quad\quad\quad\quad x = \dfrac{5}{2}$ *Dividing both sides by 2*

$\quad\quad\quad\quad x = 2\dfrac{1}{2}$

(d) $5x - 8 = 22$

$5x = 22 + 8$ *Adding 8 to both sides*

$5x = 30$

$x = \dfrac{30}{5}$ *Dividing both sides by 5*

$x = 6$

Example 4

One of the following statements is *not* an identity. Which one?

A $\dfrac{x+y}{2} \equiv \dfrac{x}{2} + \dfrac{y}{2}$

B $x - y \equiv y - x$

C $x^2 + y^2 \equiv (x+y)^2 - 2xy$

Solution

An identity will be true for any pair of values x and y. We could test each statement with $x = 5$ and $y = 10$.

Left-hand-side of A $=$ $\dfrac{x+y}{2} = \dfrac{5+10}{2} = \dfrac{15}{2} = 7.5$

Right-hand-side of A $=$ $\dfrac{x}{2} + \dfrac{y}{2} = \dfrac{5}{2} + \dfrac{10}{2} = 2.5 + 5 = 7.5$

Therefore LHS of A = RHS of A if $x = 5$ and $y = 10$.

LHS of B $=$ $x - y = 5 - 10 = -5$

RHS of B $=$ $y - x = 10 - 5 = 5$

Therefore LHS of A $\neq$ RHS of A if $x = 5$ and $y = 10$.

LHS of C $= x^2 + y^2 = 5^2 + 10^2 = 25 + 100 = 125$

RHS of C $= (x+y)^2 - 2xy = (5+10)^2 - 2 \times 5 \times 10 = 15^2 - 100$

      $= 225 - 100 = 125$

Therefore LHS of C = RHS of C if $x = 5$ and $y = 10$.

So statement B is *not* an identity. We have *not proved* that A and C are identities, but we know that they are true for certain values of x and y.

Exercises

1. Solve the following equations:

   (a) $4x = 12$ (b) $x - 5 = 8$ (c) $x + 3 = 9$

   (d) $15 + x = 20$ (e) $x - 3 = 9$ (f) $\dfrac{x}{2} = 7$

   (g) $x + 7 = 22$ (h) $5x = 30$ (i) $\dfrac{x}{4} = 9$

2. Solve the following equations:

   (a) $2x + 1 = 11$ (b) $4x - 3 = 21$ (c) $5x - 6 = 4$

   (d) $5x - 9 = 26$ (e) $9x + 21 = 102$ (f) $10x - 5 = 35$

   (g) $\dfrac{x}{2} + 3 = 4$ (h) $\dfrac{x}{7} - 9 = 2$ (i) $\dfrac{x}{2} + 3 = 11$

   (j) $x + 6 = 5$ (k) $4x + 20 = 10$ (l) $\dfrac{x}{4} + 9 = 4$

3. In this question, use the formula,

   $$C = \frac{5}{9}(F - 32)$$

   Calculate C if:

   (a) $F = 77$ (b) $F = 68$ (c) $F = 158$

4. In this question, use the formula,

   $$v = u + at$$

   Calculate v if:

   (a) $u = 2,\ a = 3$ and $t = 7$

   (b) $u = 3.2,\ a = 0.8$ and $t = 5$

   (c) $u = 30,\ a = 4$ and $t = 22$

   (d) $u = 3.6,\ a = -0.2$ and $t = 40$

5. The formula for the area of a trapezium is,

   $$A = \frac{1}{2}(a + b)h$$

   Calculate A if:

   (a) $a = 4,\ b = 10$ and $h = 6$ (b) $a = 2,\ b = 10$ and $h = 13$

   (c) $a = 3.2,\ b = 2.8$ and $h = 3.2$ (d) $a = 4,\ b = 2.5$ and $h = 7.2$

6. If $a = 6$, $b = 7.5$ and $c = -2$, calculate:

(a) $a + b + c$

(b) $ab + c$

(c) $2a + 3b$

(d) $a + 2b + 3c$

(e) ac

(f) $a^2 + b^2$

(g) $a^2 + c^2$

(h) $ab + bc$

(i) $a(b - c)$

7. A formula states:

$$y = 4x - 5$$

(a) Calculate y if $x = 3$.

(b) Determine x if $y = 23$.

(c) Determine x if $y = 8$.

8. The mean of three numbers is calculated using the formula,

$$m = \frac{x + y + z}{3}$$

(a) Calculate m if $x = 8$, $y = 17$ and $z = 2$.

(b) Determine x if $m = 5$, $y = 6$ and $z = 7$.

(c) Determine z if $m = 18$, $x = 19$ and $y = 20$.

9. Use the formula $C = \dfrac{5}{9}(F - 32)$ to determine F when:

(a) $C = 100$

(b) $C = 60$

(c) $C = 0$

10. Which of the following statements are *not* identities?

A $\qquad \dfrac{x}{y} \equiv \dfrac{y}{x}$

B $\qquad x \times y \equiv y \times x$

C $\qquad (x - y)^2 \equiv (y - x)^2$

D $\qquad (a + b)^2 \equiv (a - b)^2$

E $\qquad 2xy \equiv (x + y)^2 - x^2 - y^2$

11.   Jenny is holding a row of cubes.

You cannot see exactly how many cubes she is holding.

Call the number of cubes she is holding *n*.

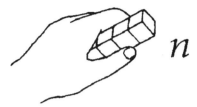

(a)   She joins on *two more* cubes.

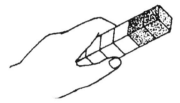

Write an expression for the total number of cubes she is holding now.

(b)   Jenny starts again with *n* cubes.

One cube is *removed*.

Write an expression for the number of cubes she is holding now.

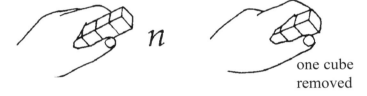

(c)   Jenny starts again with *n* cubes.

Another row of the same length is *joined on*.

Write an expression for the total number of cubes she is holding now.

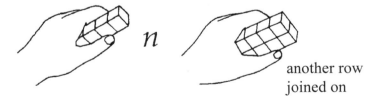

(d)   Jacob also has some cubes in his hands.

In one hand there are $2n - 1$.

In the other hand there are $2(n - 1)$ cubes.

Is Jacob holding the same number of cubes in each hand?
Explain your answer.

(KS3/97/Ma/Tier 5-7/P1)

12. (a)   Elin has a bag of marbles.

You cannot see how many marbles
are inside the bag.

Call the number of marbles which
Elin starts with in her bag n.

Elin puts 5 more marbles *into* her bag.

Write an expression to show the total
number of marbles in Elin's bag now.

(b)   Ravi has another bag of marbles.

Call the number of marbles which
Ravi starts with in his bag t.

Ravi takes 2 marbles *out* of his bag.

Write an expression to show the total
number of marbles in Ravi's bag now.

(c)   Jill has 3 bags of marbles.

Each bag has p marbles inside.

Jill takes some marbles out.

Now the total number of marbles in Jill's 3 bags is $3p - 6$.

Some of the statements below *could* be true.
Write down the letter of each statement which *could* be true.

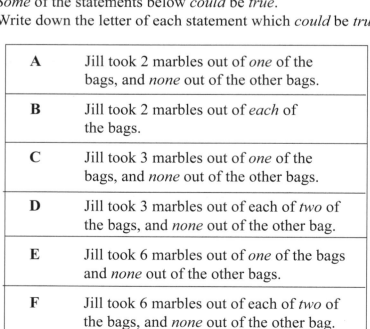

A	Jill took 2 marbles out of *one* of the bags, and *none* out of the other bags.
B	Jill took 2 marbles out of *each* of the bags.
C	Jill took 3 marbles out of *one* of the bags, and *none* out of the other bags.
D	Jill took 3 marbles out of each of *two* of the bags, and *none* out of the other bag.
E	Jill took 6 marbles out of *one* of the bags and *none* out of the other bags.
F	Jill took 6 marbles out of each of *two* of the bags, and *none* out of the other bag.

(KS3/98/Ma/Tier 5-7/P1)

13. In these walls each brick is made by *adding* the *two* bricks underneath it.

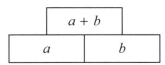

(a) Write an expression for the top brick in this wall.
     Write your expression as simply as possible.

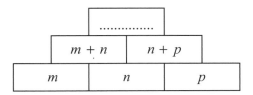

(b) Make a copy of the walls shown below and fill in the missing
     expressions.
     Write your expressions as simply as possible.

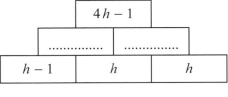

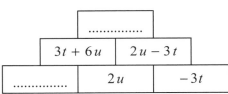

(c) In the wall below, h, j and k can be any whole numbers.

     Explain why the top brick of the wall must *always* be an *even* number.

     You can copy the wall and fill in the missing expressions if you want to.

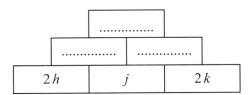

(KS3/97/Ma/Tier 5-7/P2)

11.2 Simplifying Expressions

In this section we look at how to simplify expressions, in particular, how to remove brackets from both formulae and equations.

Collecting like terms

Examples

$$a + a + a = 3a$$

$$a + b + a = 2a + b$$

$$2y + 8y = 10y$$

$$x + x^2 + x^2 = x + 2x^2$$

Only like terms can be collected

Example 1

Simplify the following expressions,

(a) $4a + 2b + 3a + 6b$ (b) $3x - 4y + 2x - y$

(c) $x^2 + 4x + 2x^2 - x$ (d) $4a^2 + a + 2a^2 - 3a$

Solution

(a) $4a + 2b + 3a + 6b = 7a + 8b$ (b) $3x - 4y + 2x - y = 5x - 5y$

(c) $x^2 + 4x + 2x^2 - x = 3x^2 + 3x$ (d) $4a^2 + a + a^2 - 3a = 6a^2 - 2a$

Expanding Brackets

Every term in each bracket must be multiplied by every other item.

$$x(4x + 2) = x \times 4x + x \times 2$$
$$= 4x^2 + 2x$$

$$(x + 1)(x + 4) = x \times x + x \times 4 + 1 \times x + 1 \times 4$$
$$= x^2 + 4x + x + 4$$
$$= x^2 + 5x + 4$$

Alternatively, you can expand brackets using the 'box' method, as shown opposite.

$$(x + 1)(x + 4) = x^2 + 1x + 4x + 4 = x^2 + 5x + 4$$

$\times$	x	$+1$
x	x^2	$+1x$
$+4$	$+4x$	$+4$

Example 2

Expand each of the following:

(a) $2(x + 3)$

(b) $4(2x - 6)$

(c) $x(x + 2)$

(d) $2x(3x - 2)$

Solution

(a) $2(x + 3) = 2 \times x + 2 \times 3$

$= 2x + 6$

(b) $4(2x - 6) = 4 \times 2x - 4 \times 6$

$= 8x - 24$

(c) $x(x + 2) = x \times x + x \times 2$

$= x^2 + 2x$

(d) $2x(3x - 2) = 2x \times 3x - 2x \times 2$

$= 6x^2 - 4x$

Example 3

Expand,

(a) $(x + 6)(x + 3)$

(b) $(x + 4)(2x - 5)$

Solution

(a) $(x + 6)(x + 3) = x \times x + x \times 3 + 6 \times x + 6 \times 3$

$= x^2 + 3x + 6x + 18$

$= x^2 + 9x + 18$

or alternatively, using the box method,

$\times$	x	$+6$
x	x^2	$+6x$
$+3$	$+3x$	$+18$

$(x + 6)(x + 3) = x^2 + 6x + 3x + 18 = x^2 + 9x + 18$

(b) $(x + 4)(2x - 5) = x \times 2x - x \times 5 + 4 \times 2x - 4 \times 5$

$= 2x^2 - 5x + 8x - 20$

$= 2x^2 + 3x - 20$

Again, using the box method,

×	x	$+4$
$2x$	$2x^2$	$+8x$
-5	$-5x$	-20

$$(x + 4)(2x - 5) = 2x^2 + 8x - 5x - 20 = 2x^2 + 3x - 20$$

Exercises

1. Simplify each of the following by collecting like terms:

   (a) $4a + b + 2a$ (b) $4b + 2c + 6b + 3c$

   (c) $4a + 5b - a + 2b$ (d) $14p + 11q - 8p + 3q$

   (e) $6x - 4y + 8x + 9y$ (f) $11x + 8y + 3z - 2y + 4z$

   (g) $16x - 8y - 3x - 4y$ (h) $11y + 12z - 10y + 4z + 2y$

2. Simplify each of the following:

   (a) $3x + 3x^2 + 4x - x^2$ (b) $4y^2 + 4y - 2y^2 + 3y$

   (c) $a^2 + a + 3a^2 - 2a$ (d) $6x^2 + 12x - 9x^2 + 3x$

3. Expand each of the following expressions by multiplying out the brackets:

   (a) $3(x + 6)$ (b) $4(x + 2)$ (c) $3(x - 1)$

   (d) $4(2x + 5)$ (e) $6(3x - 5)$ (f) $7(2x - 5)$

   (g) $6(4 - 2x)$ (h) $8(3 - 5x)$ (i) $9(5x + 10)$

4. Simplify each of the following expressions:

   (a) $2(x + 3) + 4(x + 4)$ (b) $5(x - 6) + 2(x + 3)$

   (c) $4(6 - x) + 7(2x + 1)$ (d) $11(x - 2) + 4(7x + 3)$

   (e) $8(x - 6) + 4(7 - x)$ (f) $3(4 - 5x) + 6(3x - 2)$

5. Expand each of the following expressions by multiplying out the brackets:

   (a) $x(x + 3)$ (b) $x(6x + 1)$ (c) $x(3x - 2)$

   (d) $2x(4 - x)$ (e) $6x(2x + 4)$ (f) $5x(3x - 7)$

   (g) $11x(x - 3)$ (h) $14x(2 + 3x)$ (i) $6x(4 - 2x)$

6. Expand each of the following expressions by multiplying out the brackets:

   (a) $(x + 4)(x + 3)$ (b) $(x + 2)(x + 4)$ (c) $(x + 1)(x + 5)$

   (d) $(x + 6)(x - 1)$ (e) $(x - 4)(x + 2)$ (f) $(x - 3)(x + 2)$

   (g) $(x - 4)(x - 5)$ (h) $(x - 3)(x - 2)$ (i) $(x - 7)(x - 9)$

7. Simplify each of the following expressions:

   (a) $(x + 2)(x + 4) + (x + 1)(x + 2)$

   (b) $(x + 3)(x + 7) + (x - 1)(x + 5)$

   (c) $(x + 6)(x + 2) - (x - 2)(x + 3)$

   (d) $(x - 4)(x - 8) - (x - 1)(x - 9)$

8. Expand each expression:

   (a) $(2x + 1)(3x + 2)$ (b) $(4x - 7)(2x + 1)$

   (c) $(3x + 5)(2x - 8)$ (d) $(4x + 5)(3x - 8)$

   (e) $(8x + 2)(3x - 3)$ (f) $(6x - 5)(3x - 7)$

9. Simplify:

   (a) $(3x + 2)(5x + 9) + (4x - 2)(3x - 5)$

   (b) $(4x + 6)(5x + 1) - (2x + 3)(3x + 1)$

   (c) $(6x - 5)(x + 1) - (2x + 7)(3x - 5)$

10. Expand:

   (a) $(x + 1)^2$ (b) $(x - 2)^2$ (c) $(x + 3)^2$

   (d) $(x + 5)^2$ (e) $(x - 7)^2$ (f) $(x - 8)^2$

   (g) $(x + 10)^2$ (h) $(x - 12)^2$ (i) $(x + 4)^2$

   (j) $(2x + 3)^2$ (k) $(4x - 7)$ (l) $(3x + 2)^2$

   (m) $(4x + 1)^2$ (n) $(5x - 2)^2$ (o) $(6x - 4)^2$

11.   Expand:

   (a) $(x + 1)(x - 1)$ (b) $(x + 3)(x - 3)$

   (c) $(x + 7)(x - 7)$ (d) $(x + 9)(x - 9)$

   (e) $(x + 12)(x - 12)$ (f) $(2x + 1)(2x - 1)$

   (g) $(3x + 2)(3x - 2)$ (h) $(4x + 7)(4x - 7)$

12.   Expand:

   (a) $(x + 1)^3$ (b) $(2x + 1)^3$ (c) $(x - 5)^3$

13.   Here are some algebra cards:

   (a)   One of the cards will always give the same answer as $\boxed{\dfrac{n}{2}}$.

         Which card is it?

   (b)   One of the cards will always give the same answer as $\boxed{n \times n}$.

         Which card is it?

   (c)   *Two* of the cards will always give the same answer as $\boxed{2 \times n}$.

         Which cards are they?

   (d)   Write a *new* card which will always give the same answer as

         $\boxed{3n + 2n}$.

(KS3/97/Ma/Tier 5-7/P1)

14. (a) (i) The diagram shows a rectangle 18 cm long and 14 cm wide.
It has been split into *four smaller rectangles,* A, B, C and D.
Write down the *area* of each of the small rectangles.
One has been done for you.

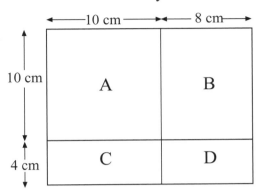

Area of Rectangle C = 40 cm^2.

(ii) What is the area of the *whole* rectangle?

(iii) What is 18×14 ?

(b) (i) The diagram shows a rectangle $(n + 3)$ cm long and
$(n + 2)$ cm wide.
It has been split into *four smaller rectangles.*
Write down a *number* or an *expression* for the *area* of *each small
rectangle.*
One has been done for you.

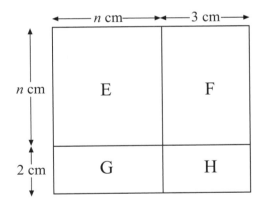

Area of Rectangle F = $3n$ cm^2.

(ii) What is $(n + 3)(n + 2)$ multiplied out?

(KS3/99/Ma/Tier 5-7/P1)

15. Multiply out and simplify these expressions:

    (a) $3(x-2)-2(4-3x)$

    (b) $(x+2)(x+3)$

    (c) $(x+4)(x-1)$

    (d) $(x-2)^2$

                                                                            (KS3/98/Ma/Tier 6-8/P1)

16. A number grid is inside a large triangle.
    The small triangles are numbered consecutively.
    The diagram shows the first 4 rows.

    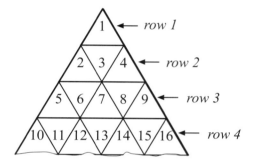

    (a) An expression for the *last* number in row n is n^2.

         Write an expression for the *last but one* number
         in row n.

    (b) An expression for the *first* number in row n is n^2-2n+2.
         Calculate the value of the first number in *row 10*.

    (c) Make a copy of the table and complete it by writing an expression:

first number in row n	n^2-2n+2
second number in row n	

    (d) Make a copy of the table and complete it by writing an expression:

centre number in *row* n	n^2-n+1
centre number in *row*	$(n+1)^2-(n+1)+1$

    (e) Multiply out and simplify the expression $(n+1)^2-(n+1)+1$.
         Show your working.

                                                                            (KS3/99/Ma/Tier 6-8/P1)

11.3 Factorising

In this section we consider examples of the process of factorising, whereby the process of removing brackets is reversed and brackets are introduced into expressions.

Example 1

Factorise:

(a) $8x + 12$ (b) $35x + 28$

Solution

(a)   Note that both terms are multiples of 4, so we can write,

$$8x + 12 = 4(2x + 3)$$

(b)   Here both terms are multiples of 7, so

$$35x + 28 = 7(5x + 4)$$

Results like this can be checked by multiplying out the bracket to get back to the original expression.

Example 2

Factorise,

(a) $x^2 + 2x$ (b) $3x^2 - 9x$ (c) $x^3 - x^2$

Solution

(a)   Here, as both terms are multiples of x, we can write,
$$x^2 + 2x = x(x + 2)$$

(b)   In this case, both terms are multiples of x and 3, giving,
$$3x^2 - 9x = 3x(x - 3)$$

(c)   In this example, both terms are multiples of x^2,
$$x^3 - x^2 = x^2(x - 1)$$

Sometimes it is possible to factorise in stages. For example, in part (b), you could have worked like this:

$$3x^2 - 9x = 3(x^2 - 3x)$$
$$= 3x(x - 3)$$

Example 3

Factorise:

(a) $x^2 + 9x + 18$ (b) $x^2 + 2x - 15$ (c) $x^2 - 7x + 12$

Solution

(a) This expression will need to be factorised into two brackets:

$$x^2 + 9x + 18 = (x \quad)(x \quad)$$

As the expression begins x^2, both brackets must begin with x. The two numbers to go in the brackets must multiply together to give 18 and add to give 9. So they must be 3 and 6, giving,

$$x^2 + 9x + 18 = (x + 3)(x + 6)$$

You can check this result by multiplying out the brackets.

(b) We note first that two brackets are needed and that both must contain an x, as shown:

$$x^2 + 2x - 15 = (x \quad)(x \quad)$$

Two other numbers are needed which, when multiplied give -15 and when added give 2. In this case, these are -3 and 5. So the factorisation is,

$$x^2 + 2x - 15 = (x - 3)(x + 5)$$

Check this result by multiplying out the brackets.

(c) Again, we begin by noting that,

$$x^2 - 7x + 12 = (x \quad)(x \quad)$$

We require two numbers which, when multiplied give 12 and when added give -7. In this case, these numbers are -3 and -4.

$$x^2 - 7x + 12 = (x - 3)(x - 4)$$

Exercises

1. Factorise:

(a) $4x - 2$	(b) $6x - 12$	(c) $5x - 20$
(d) $4x + 32$	(e) $6x - 8$	(f) $8 - 12x$
(g) $21x - 14$	(h) $15x + 20$	(i) $30 - 10x$

2. Factorise:

(a) $x^2 + 4x$	(b) $x^2 - 3x$	(c) $4x - x^2$
(d) $6x^2 + 8x$	(e) $9x^2 + 15x$	(f) $7x^2 - 21x$
(g) $28x - 35x^2$	(h) $6x^2 - 14x$	(i) $5x^2 - 3x$

3. Factorise:

   (a) $x^3 + x^2$ (b) $2x^2 - x^3$ (c) $4x^3 - 2x^2$

   (d) $8x^3 + 4x^2$ (e) $16x^2 - 36x^3$ (f) $4x^3 + 22x^2$

   (g) $16x^2 - 6x^3$ (h) $14x^3 + 21x^2$ (i) $28x^3 - 49x^2$

4. (a) Expand $(x + 5)(x - 5)$.

   (b) Factorise $x^2 - 25$.

   (c) Factorise each of the following:

        (i) $x^2 - 49$ (ii) $x^2 - 64$ (iii) $x^2 - 100$

        (iv) $x^2 - a^2$ (v) $x^2 - 4b^2$

5. Factorise:

   (a) $x^2 + 7x + 12$ (b) $x^2 + 8x + 7$ (c) $x^2 + 11x + 18$

   (d) $x^2 + 12x + 27$ (e) $x^2 + 17x + 70$ (f) $x^2 + 6x + 8$

   (g) $x^2 + 16x + 28$ (h) $x^2 + 18x + 77$ (i) $x^2 + 16x + 63$

6. Factorise:

   (a) $x^2 + x - 2$ (b) $x^2 + x - 20$ (c) $x^2 - x - 12$

   (d) $x^2 - 13x + 36$ (e) $x^2 - 10x + 16$ (f) $x^2 + x - 42$

   (g) $x^2 + 13x - 30$ (h) $x^2 - 17x + 72$ (i) $x^2 - 2x - 99$

7. The area of the rectangle shown is $x^2 - 5x$.

   Express a in terms of x.

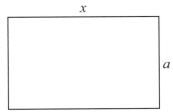

8. The area of the rectangle shown is $x^2 + 11x + 30$.

   Express a in terms of x.

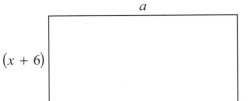

9. The area of the triangle shown is

$$\frac{1}{2}x^2 + \frac{3}{2}x - 5.$$

Express h in terms of x.

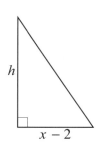

10. The area of the trapezium shown is

$$\frac{1}{2}x^2 + 10x + 18.$$

Determine a.

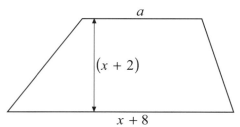

11.4   Using Formulae

In this section we make use of formulae and develop simple formulae ourselves. First we begin with some revision of working with *negative numbers*.

Example 1

If $a = 6$, $b = -5$, $c = -7$ and $d = 3$, calculate:

(a) $a + c$ (b) $a - b$ (c) bc (d) $b^2 + cd$

Solution

(a) $\begin{aligned} a + c &= 6 + (-7) \\ &= 6 - 7 \\ &= -1 \end{aligned}$

(b) $\begin{aligned} a - b &= 6 - (-5) \\ &= 6 + 5 \\ &= 11 \end{aligned}$

(c) $\begin{aligned} bc &= (-5) \times (-7) \\ &= 35 \end{aligned}$

(d) $\begin{aligned} b^2 + cd &= (-5)^2 + (-7) \times 3 \\ &= 25 + (-21) \\ &= 25 - 21 \\ &= 4 \end{aligned}$

Example 2

A triangle has sides of length x, $x + 4$ and $x + 8$, as shown in the diagram.

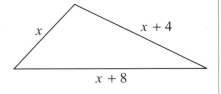

(a) Write down a formula for the perimeter, p, of the triangle.

(b) Calculate the perimeter when $x = 10$.

(c) Calculate x when the perimeter is 45.

Solution

(a) $p = x + (x + 4) + (x + 8)$

  $p = 3x + 12$

(b) $p = 3 \times 10 + 12$

  $p = 30 + 12$

  $p = 42$

(c) $45 = 3x + 12$

  $33 = 3x$ *Subtracting 12 from both sides*

  $x = \dfrac{33}{3}$ *Dividing both sides by 3*

  $x = 11$

Example 3

A removal firm charges £80 plus £2 for every mile that their removal van travels.

(a) Write down a formula for the cost, £C, of a move of n miles.

(b) Calculate the cost of moving 262 miles.

(c) A move costs £500. How far did the removal van travel?

Solution

(a) $C = 80 + 2n$

(b) $C = 80 + 262 \times 2$

  $C = 80 + 524$

  $C = £604$

(c) $500 = 80 + 2n$

  $420 = 2n$ *Subtracting 80 from both sides*

  $n = \dfrac{420}{2}$ *Dividing both sides by 2*

  $n = 210$ miles, so the van travelled 210 miles.

Exercises

1. If $p = 6$, $q = -2$, $r = 12$ and $s = -5$, calculate:

   (a) $p + q$ (b) $p - s$ (c) $r - q$

   (d) $q^2 + s^2$ (e) $p - r$ (f) $r + s^2$

   (g) $pq + r$ (h) $r - qs$ (i) $2r + 5q$

   (j) $6q - 2p$ (k) $4s - 2r$ (l) $3q + 7s$

2. The diagram shows a quadrilateral.

   (a) Write down a formula for the perimeter, p, of the quadrilateral.

   (b) Calculate the perimeter if $x = 14$.

   (c) Determine x if the perimeter is 73.

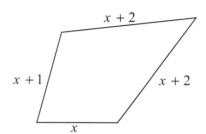

3. The diagram shows a parallelogram.

   (a) Write down a formula for the perimeter, p, of the parallelogram.

   (b) Calculate the perimeter when $x = 7$.

   (c) Determine x if the perimeter is 182.

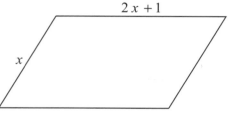

4. The diagram shows a kite.

   (a) Write down a formula for the perimeter, p, of the kite.

   (b) Calculate the perimeter if $x = 9$.

   (c) Determine x if the perimeter is 118.

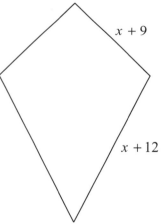

5. The semi-circle shown has radius r.

   (a) Write down formulae for the area and perimeter of the semi-circle, giving your answers correct to 2 decimal places.

   (b) Calculate the area and perimeter if $r = 5$ cm.

   (c) Determine r if the perimeter is 40 cm.

   (d) Determine r if the area is 18 cm^2.

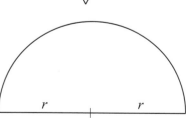

6. A taxi firm charges £1.80 plus 50p per mile travelled.

    (a) Write down a formula for the cost, C pence, of travelling m miles.

    (b) Calculate the cost of a 3-mile journey.

    (c) The charge for a journey is £6. What is the distance travelled?

7. Ahmed runs a baked potato stall at the market. He makes a profit of 40p on each potato he sells but he has to pay £50 each day for the stall.

    (a) Write down a formula for the amount of money, in pounds, Ahmed makes on one day if he sells x potatoes.

    (b) Describe what happens if $x = 200$.

    (c) Describe what happens if $x = 100$.

    (d) How many potatoes must he sell to make a profit of £100 in one day?

8. Records for the weather suggest that on average, it is $22\,°C$ warmer in Miami than in Washington.

    The average temperature in Miami in $°C$ is M.

    The average temperature in Washington in $°C$ is W.

    (a) Write down a formula for M in terms of W.

    (b) Write down a formula for W in terms of M.

    (c) Determine M if W is -7.

    (d) Determine W if M is -3.

9. An engineer charges £20 plus £p per hour to repair central heating boilers. At one house a repair takes 3 hours and costs £71.

    (a) Determine the value of p.

    (b) Write down a formula for the cost, £C, of a repair that takes x hours.

    (c) A repair costs £96.50. How long does it take?

10. Alan claims that the two shapes shown have the same area.

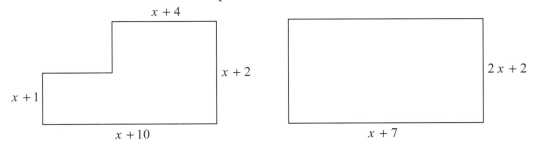

    (a) Determine a formula for the area of each shape.

    (b) Is Alan correct?

11. Ice creams are sold as cones or tubs at the Beach Kiosk.
     A cone costs 60 pence.
     A tub costs 40 pence.

     The income (F) in pence of the Beach Kiosk can be calculated from the
     equation $F = 60x + 40y$ where x is the number of cones sold and y is
     the number of tubs sold.

     (a) On June 1st 1994, $x = 65$ and $y = 80$.

          Work out the income.
          Show your working.

     (b) On June 2nd 1994, $F = 4800$ and $x = 50$.

          Work out how many tubs were sold.
          Show your working.

     (c) During the first week of last summer 950 ice creams were sold.
          437 of them were tubs.

          What percentage of the ice creams sold were tubs?

     (d) *Estimate* the total income in pounds for the summer of 1995 using the
          information in the box.

          > Last summer 14 723 ice creams were sold.
          > Roughly the same number of ice creams is likely
          > to be sold in the summer of 1995.
          > The ratio of cones to tubs sold is likely to be about 1 : 1.
          > The cost of a cone is to stay at 60 pence.
          > The cost of a tub is to stay at 40 pence.

          (i)   Write down the number you will use instead of 14 723.
          (ii) Write down the value you will use for the cost of an ice cream.
          (iii) Write down your estimate of the total income for the summer
                of 1995.

                                                            (KS3/95/Ma/Levels 5-7/P1)

12. A robot accelerates at a constant rate. It can move backwards or forwards.

     When the robot moves, three equations connect the following:

     u   its initial speed in m/s
     v   its final speed in m/s
     a   its acceleration in m/s^2
     s   the distance travelled in m
     t   the time taken in seconds

     The equations are:

     $$v = u + at \qquad\qquad v^2 = u^2 + 2as \qquad\qquad s = ut + \frac{1}{2}at^2$$

For a journey made by the robot:

u = 0.25 m/s   t = 3.5 seconds   a = − 0.05 m/s

Use the appropriate equation to find:

(a)   The distance travelled.
        Show your working.

(b)   The robot's final speed.
        Show your working.

(KS3/95/Ma/Levels 6-8/P2)

13.   Magic squares were used to tell fortunes long ago in China.
        They contain whole numbers starting from 1.
        The numbers in each row add up to the magic number.

Eleri's magic square has 3 rows.
The magic number is 15.
The size is 3×3.

8	1	6
3	5	7
4	9	2

magic number 15

Tony made a magic square with more rows.
The magic number is 2925.
We do not know the size of his square.

magic number 2925

(a)   When the size of a magic square is $n \times n$,

        the magic number is $\dfrac{n\left(n^{2} + 1\right)}{2}$.

        Use $n = 3$ to check that this works for Eleri's magic square.

(b)   Find the size of Tony's magic square.
        You may use trial and improvement.

(KS3/94/Ma/5-7/P2)

14. Alan throws a ball to Katie who is standing 20 m away.
     The ball is thrown and caught at a height of 2.0 m above the ground.

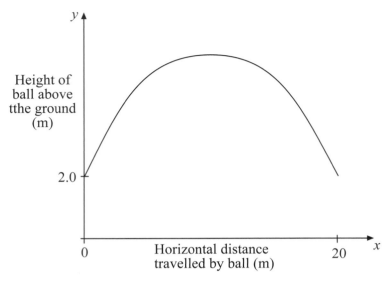

The ball follows the curve with equation

$$y = 6 + c(10 - x)^2 \text{ where } c \text{ is a constant.}$$

(a) Calculate the value of c by substituting $x = 0$, $y = 2$ into the
     equation.
     Show your working.

Alan throws the ball to Katie again, but this time the ball hits the ground
before it reaches her.

The ball follows the curve with equation $y = -0.1(x^2 - 6x - 16)$

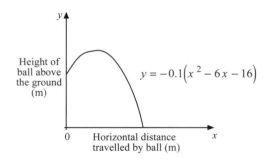

(b) Calculate the height above the ground at which the ball left Alan's
     hand.
     Show your working.

(KS3/97/Ma/Tier 6-8/P1)

12 Constructions and Loci

12.1 Recap: Angles and Scale Drawing

The concepts in this unit rely heavily on knowledge acquired previously, particularly for angles and scale drawings, so in this first section we revise these two topics.

Example 1

In the diagram opposite, determine the size of each of the unknown angles.

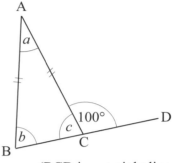

Solution

Since

$$c + 100° = 180° \text{ (BCD is a straight line)}$$

$$c = 180° - 100°$$

$$c = 80°$$

(BCD is a straight line.)

Also, $b = c$, since the triangle is isosceles, so $b = 80°$.

Finally, since

$$a + b + c = 180° \text{ (angles in a triangle add up to } 180°\text{)}$$

then

$$a = 180° - (80° + 80°)$$

so $a = 20°$

Example 2

In the diagram opposite, given that $a = 65°$, determine the size of each of the unknown angles.

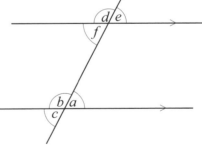

Solution

$b = 180° - a$ (angles on a straight line are supplementary, i.e. they add up to $180°$)

$b = 180° - 65°$

$b = 115°$

$c = a = 65°$ (vertically opposite angles)

$d = b = 115°$ (corresponding angles, as the lines are parallel)

$e = a = 65°$ (corresponding angles)

$f = a = 65°$ (alternate angles)

Example 3

Draw an accurate plan of the car park which is sketched here. Use the scale

$$1 \text{ cm} \equiv 10 \text{ m}.$$

Estimate the distance AB.

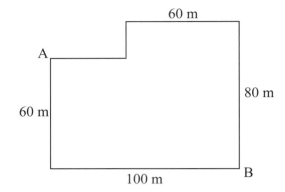

Solution

The equivalent lengths are:

$$100 \text{ m} \equiv 10 \text{ cm}, \quad 80 \text{ m} \equiv 8 \text{ cm}, \quad 60 \text{ m} \equiv 6 \text{ cm},$$

giving the following scale drawing:

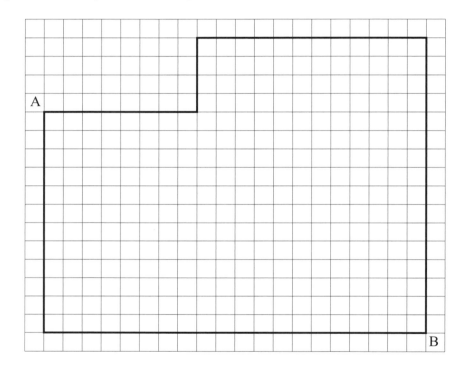

In the scale drawing, AB = 11.7 cm, which gives an actual distance AB = 117 m in the car park.

Exercises

1. Determine the size of each of the angles marked with a letter in the following diagrams, giving reasons for your answers.

   (a)

   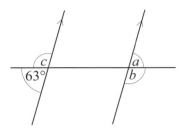

   (b)

   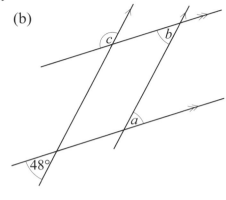

2. Determine the size of each of the angles marked with a letter in the following diagram:

   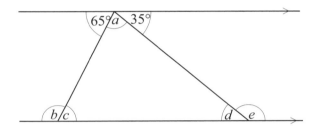

3. BCDE is a trapezium. Determine the size of each of the angles marked with a letter in the diagram, giving reasons for your answers.

   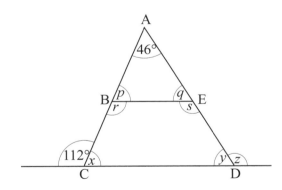

4. Draw a scale drawing of the running track shown in the sketch below. The radius of the semicircles is 45 m.

   Use a scale of

   $1 \text{ cm} \equiv 10 \text{ m}.$

   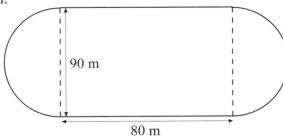

5.   (a)   The time on this clock is 3 o'clock.

What is the *size* of the *angle* between the hands?

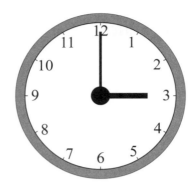

(b)   Write down the whole number missing from this sentence:

At .... o'clock the size of the angle between the hands is 180 °.

(c)   What is the size of the *angle* between the hands at 1 o'clock?

(d)   What is the size of the *angle* between the hands at 5 o'clock?

(e)   How long does it take for the *minute* hand to move 360 ° ?

(KS3/99/Ma/Tier 3-5/P2)

6.   (a)   Which *two* of these angles are the *same size*?

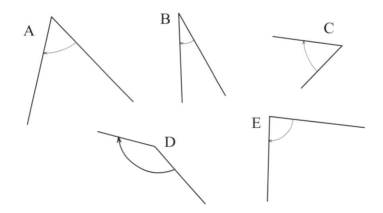

(b)   Draw an angle which is *bigger* than a *right angle*.

(c)   Kelly is facing *North*.
She turns *clockwise* through 2 right angles.
Which direction is she facing now?

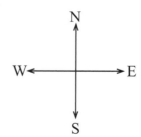

(d)   Aled is facing *West*.
He turns *clockwise* through 3 right angles.
Which direction is he facing now?

(KS3/98/Ma/Tier 3-5/P1)

7.   The shape below has 3 *identical white* tiles and 3 *identical grey* tiles.

The sides of each tile are all the same length.

Opposite sides of each tile are parallel.

One of the angles is 70 °.

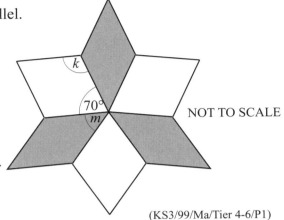

(a)   Calculate the size of *angle k*.

NOT TO SCALE

(b)   Calculate the size of *angle m*.
       Show your working.

(KS3/99/Ma/Tier 4-6/P1)

8.   Kay is drawing shapes on her computer.

(a)   She wants to draw this
       triangle. She needs to
       know angles *a, b* and *c*.

       Calculate angles *a, b* and *c*.

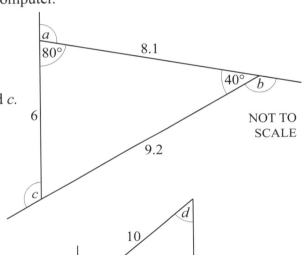

NOT TO
SCALE

(b)   Kay draws a rhombus:
       Calculate angles *d* and *e*.

NOT TO
SCALE

(c)   Kay types the instructions to draw a regular pentagon:

       repeat 5 [forward 10, left turn 72]

       Complete the following instructions to draw a regular hexagon:

       repeat 6 [forward 10, left turn ....]

(KS3/97/Ma/Tier 4-6/P1)

9.   In the scale drawing, the shaded area represents a lawn.

There is a wire fence *all around* the lawn.

The shortest distance from the fence to the edge of the lawn is *always* 6 m.

On a copy of the diagram, draw *accurately* the position of the fence.

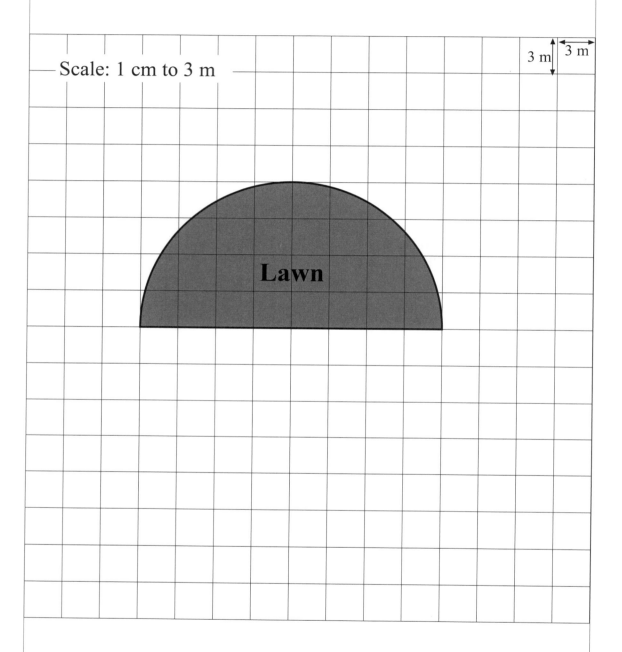

Scale: 1 cm to 3 m

Lawn

3 m   3 m

(KS3/98/Ma/Tier 6-8/P1)

10. Look at the diagram:

Side AB is the same length as side AC.

Side BD is the same length as side BC.

Calculate the value of *x*.

Show your working.

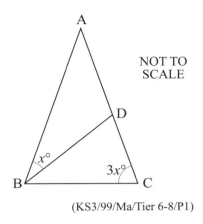

NOT TO
SCALE

(KS3/99/Ma/Tier 6-8/P1)

12.2 Constructions

In this section we look at how to construct triangles and various lines. You will
need a ruler, a protractor and a pair of compasses to be able to draw these
constructions. The following examples illustrate some of the techniques that you
will need to use.

Example 1

Construct the perpendicular bisector
of the line AB.

Then label the midpoint of AB, M.

Solution

There are many lines that cut AB
exactly in half. We have to
construct the one that is
perpendicular to AB.

We begin by drawing arcs of equal
radius, centred on the points A and
B, as shown in the diagram.
The radius of these arcs should be
roughly $\frac{2}{3}$ to $\frac{3}{4}$ of the length AB.

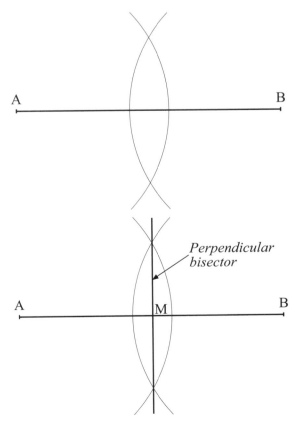

Then draw a line through the
intersection points of the two
arcs.

The point where the bisector
intersects AB can then be
labelled M.

Example 2

The diagram shows the line
AB and the point C.

Draw a line through C that
is perpendicular to AB.

Solution

Using C as the centre, draw
an arc as shown.

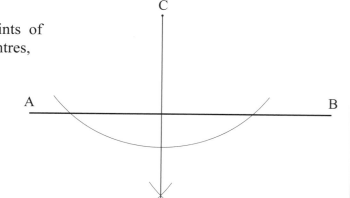

Then using the intersection points of
this arc with the line AB as centres,
draw two further arcs with
radii of equal length. The
perpendicular line can then
be drawn from C through
the point where these
two new arcs cross.

Example 3

Bisect this angle.

Solution

To bisect an angle you need to draw
a line that cuts the angle in half.

First draw an arc using O as the centre.

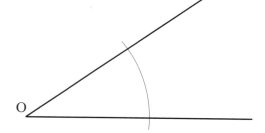

Then draw two further arcs of equal radius, using the points where the arc intersects the lines as the centres.

The bisector can then be drawn from O through the point where these two new arcs cross.

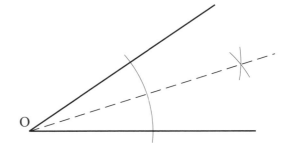

Example 4

The triangle ABC is such that AB = 8 cm, ∠BAC = 40 ° and ∠ABC = 60 °. Draw this triangle.

Solution

First draw the line AB of length 8 cm.

A ─────────────────────── B

At the left-hand-end of the line, draw the ∠ BAC which is 40 °.

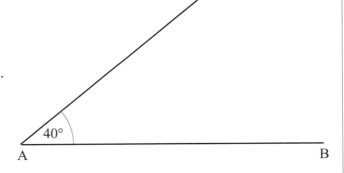

Then draw the ∠ ABC which is 60 °.

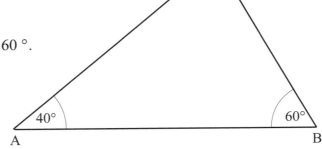

Exercises

1.   (a)   Draw a line of length 10 cm.

       (b)   Construct the perpendicular bisector of the line.

       (c)   Check that it *does* cut the line in half.

       (d)   Use a protractor to check that it *is* perpendicular.

2.   (a)   Mark 3 points, not in a straight line, on a piece of paper and label them A, B and C. Draw a line from A to B.

       (b)   Construct a line that is perpendicular to AB and passes through C.

       (c)   Use a protractor to check that your line is perpendicular.

3.   (a)   Use a ruler and a protractor to construct the triangle ABC where AB = 6 cm, $\angle ABC = 60\,°$ and $\angle BAC = 50\,°$.

       (b)   Construct a line that is perpendicular to AC and passes through the corner B.

4.   (a)   Draw a triangle with sides of length 7 cm, 4 cm and 6 cm.

       (b)   Construct the perpendicular bisector of each side. What do you notice?

       (c)   Draw a circle with its centre at the point where the lines intersect and that passes through each corner of the triangle.

       (d)   Repeat this process for any other triangle. Does it still work?

5.   (a)   Draw the triangle which has sides of length 8 cm, 7 cm and 6 cm.

       (b)   Construct the bisector of each angle of the triangle.

       (c)   Using the point where the lines intersect as its centre, draw the largest circle that will fit inside the triangle.

6.   The diagram shows how Ishmael constructed a 60 ° angle.

       (a)   Construct a 60 ° angle in this way and then check that it *is* 60 °.

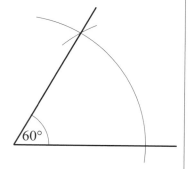

       (b)   Bisect your angle to obtain a 30 ° angle.

       (c)   Construct the following angles, using a pair of compasses and a ruler.

             (i)   120 °   (ii)   240 °   (iii)   300 °

             (iv)   90 °   (v)   270 °   (vi)   45 °

7.   The triangle ABC is such that AB = 6 cm, AC = 7 cm and ∠BAC = 50 °.

   (a)   Draw the triangle.

   (b)   What is the length of the side BC ?

   (c)   Construct a line that passes through C and is perpendicular to AB.

   (d)   Hence calculate the area of the triangle.

8.   A triangle PQR has PR = 6 cm, QR = 5 cm and ∠ QPR = 45 °. Abigail and
      Kirsty are asked to draw this triangle. They draw the two triangles below.

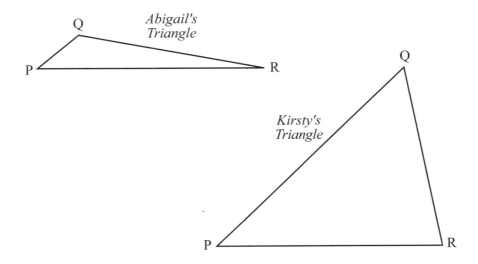

   (a)   Are they both correct?

   (b)   Draw the two possible triangles ABC, given the information below.

                 AB   = 8 cm

                 BC   = 7 cm

                 ∠ BAC = 50 °

9.   Construct each of the following triangles, without using a protractor.

   (a)   (b)

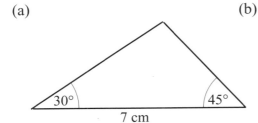

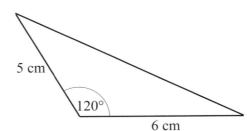

10. Draw a circle and two chords like those shown in the diagram.

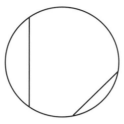

Construct the perpendicular bisector for each chord. What do you notice?

Do you think this will always be true?

11. Here is a *rough sketch* of a sector of a circle.

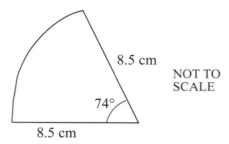

8.5 cm

NOT TO
SCALE

74°

8.5 cm

Make an *accurate, full size* drawing of this sector.

(KS3/97/Ma/Tier 5-7/P2)

12. Jane wants to design a toy engine.

She makes a rough sketch to show some of the measurements.

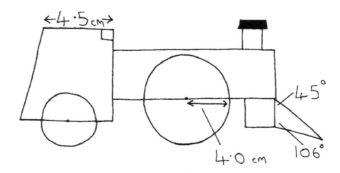

Jane starts to draw the accurate side view.

On a copy of the following diagram, finish Jane's side view.

You will need a ruler, an angle measurer or protractor, and a pair of compasses.

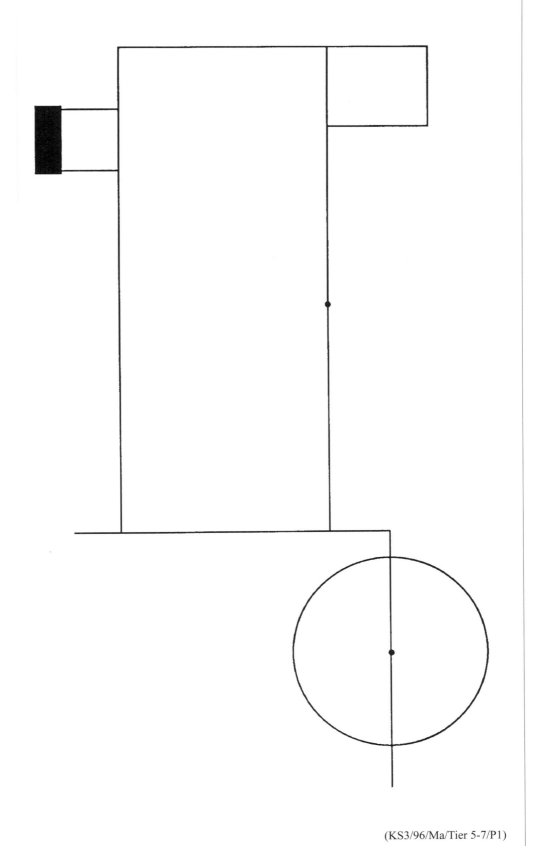

(KS3/96/Ma/Tier 5-7/P1)

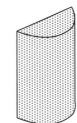

13. (a) The top and the base of this box are *semi-circles*.

Which *one* of the nets below could fold up to make a box like this?

A

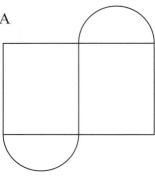

B

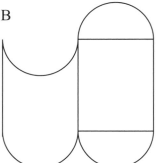

C

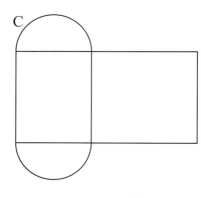

D

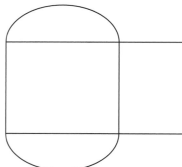

E

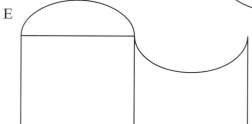

(b) This is a rough sketch of the *base* of a box.

It is a *semi-circle,* with *diameter* 8 cm.

Make an accurate, full size drawing of the *base* of the box.

You will need a ruler and a pair of compasses.

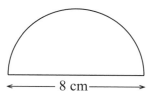

8 cm

(KS3/98/Ma/Tier 3-5/P2)

12.3 Loci

A locus is a set of points all of which share some common property. A locus may be a point, a line, a curve or a region. The important point is that all the points that make up the locus have to satisfy the same rule or condition. For example, you might be asked to draw the locus of points that are a certain distance from a given point or line.

Example 1

Draw the locus of the points that are 3 cm from the point A.

Solution

The locus will simply be a circle, centre A, with radius 3 cm. Every point on the circle will be 3 cm from A.

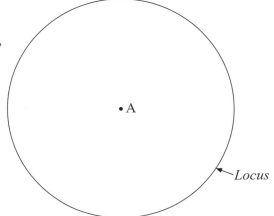

Example 2

Draw the locus of the points that are equidistant from A and B.

A•   •B

Solution

All the points must be the same distance from A as from B. The locus is the perpendicular bisector of the line AB.

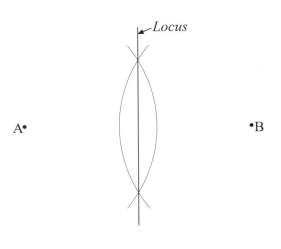

Example 3

Draw the locus of points that are 1 cm from this circle.

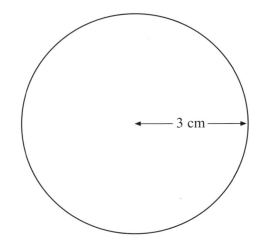

Solution

The locus is made up of 2 parts. 1 part consists of the points that are 1 cm from the circle and inside it; the other is those points that are 1 cm from the circle and are outside it.

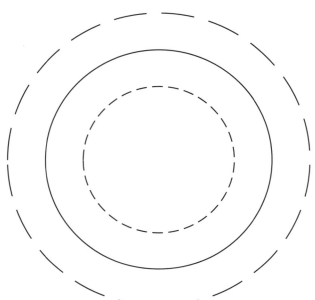

Exercises

1. (a) Draw a line of length 5 cm.

    (b) Draw the locus of points that are 1 cm from the line.

2. (a) Draw a circle of radius 2 cm.

    (b) Draw the locus of points that are 2 cm from the circle.

    (c) On your diagram, shade the locus of points that are *less* than 2 cm from the circle.

3. (a) Draw the rectangle shown in the diagram.

    (b) Draw the locus of the points that are 1 cm from the rectangle.

    (c) Repeat part (b) for a rectangle that is 6 cm long and 5 cm wide.

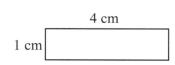

4. Construct the locus of the points that are equidistant from the two lines shown in the diagram.

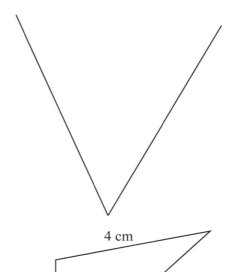

5. (a) Construct the triangle shown in the diagram.

   (b) Draw the locus of the points that are 1 cm from the triangle.

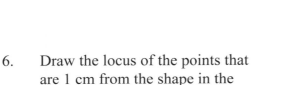

6. Draw the locus of the points that are 1 cm from the shape in the diagram.

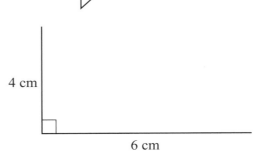

7. Two points A and B are 6 cm apart.

   (a) Draw the locus of the points that are equidistant from A and B.

   (b) Draw the locus of points that are 5 cm from B.

   (c) Indicate the points that are 5 cm from A and B.

8. The points A and B are 9 cm apart. Draw the locus of the points that are twice as far from A as they are from B.

9. (a) Construct the triangle shown in the diagram.

   (b) Draw the locus of points that are equidistant from A and B and within 3 cm of C.

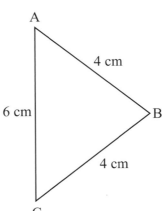

10. A ladder has length 4 m. It initially leans against a vertical wall with its base on horizontal ground.

    The ladder slides down until it is lying horizontal on the ground.

    Draw the locus of the midpoint of the ladder, using a suitable scale drawing.

11. Some pupils want to plant a tree in the school's garden.

    The tree must be at least 12 m from the school building.

    It must also be at least 10 m from the centre of the round pond.

    (a) Show accurately on a copy of the following plan the *region* in which the tree can be planted.

    Shade in this region.

    SCALE   1 cm to 2 m

    (b) The pupils want to make a gravel path of width 1 m around the pond.

    Calculate the *area* of the path.

    Show your working.

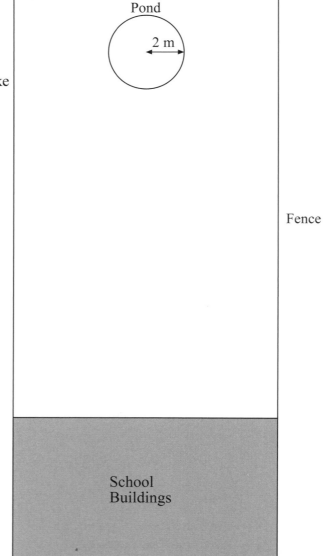

(KS3/97/Ma/Tier 6-8/P2)

13 Graphs, Equations and Inequalities

13.1 Linear Inequalities

In this section we look at how to solve linear inequalities and illustrate their solutions using a number line.

When using a number line, a small solid circle is used for $\leq$ or $\geq$ and a hollow circle is used for $>$ or $<$.

For example,

$x \geq 5$

A number line from -1 to 6 with a solid circle at 5 and an arrow pointing right.

Here the solid circle means that the value 5 is included.

$x < 7$

A number line from -4 to 7 with a hollow circle at 7 and an arrow pointing left.

Here the hollow circle means that the value 7 is not included.

When solving linear inequalities we use the same techniques as those used for solving linear equations. The important exception to this is that when *multiplying or dividing by a negative number*, you must *reverse the direction of the inequality*. However, in practice, it is best to try to avoid doing this.

Example 1

Solve the inequality $x + 6 > 3$ and illustrate the solution on a number line.

Solution

$x + 6 > 3$

$\qquad x > 3 - 6$ *Subtracting 6 from both sides of the inequality*

$x > -3$

This can be illustrated as shown below:

A number line from -4 to 3 with a hollow circle at -3 and an arrow pointing right.

Example 2

Solve the inequality $3x + 7 \geq 19$ and illustrate the solution on a number line.

Solution

$$3x + 7 \geq 19$$
$$3x \geq 12 \qquad \textit{Subtracting 7 from both sides}$$
$$x \geq 4 \qquad \textit{Dividing both sides by 3}$$

This can now be shown on a number line.

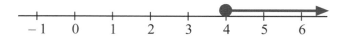

Example 3

Illustrate the solution to the inequality $12 - 3x \geq 6$.

Solution

Because this inequality contains the term '$-3x$', first add $3x$ to both sides to remove the $-$ sign.

$$12 - 3x \geq 6$$
$$12 \geq 6 + 3x \qquad \textit{Adding 3x to both sides}$$
$$6 \geq 3x \qquad \textit{Subtracting 6 from both sides}$$
$$2 \geq x \qquad \textit{Dividing both sides by 3}$$

or $\qquad x \leq 2$

This is illustrated below.

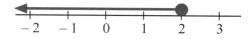

Example 4

Solve the equation $-7 < 5x + 3 \leq 23$.

Solution

In an inequality of this type you must apply the same operation to each of the 3 parts.

$$-7 < 5x + 3 \leq 23$$
$$-10 < 5x \leq 20 \qquad \textit{Subtracting 3 from both sides}$$
$$-2 < x \leq 4 \qquad \textit{Dividing both sides by 5}$$

This can then be illustrated as below.

Exercises

1. Draw diagrams to illustrate the following inequalities:

    (a) $x > 3$

    (b) $x \leq 4$

    (c) $x \leq -2$

    (d) $x \geq -3$

    (e) $-2 \leq x < 4$

    (f) $0 \leq x \leq 3$

2. Write down the inequality represented by each of the following diagrams:

    (a)

    (b)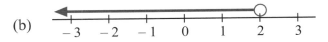

    (c)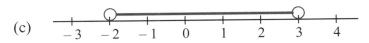

    (d)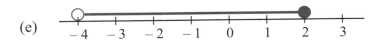

    (e)

3. Solve each of the following inequalities and illustrate the results on a number line.

    (a) $x + 7 > 12$

    (b) $x - 6 > 3$

    (c) $4x \leq 20$

    (d) $5x \geq 10$

    (e) $x + 6 \geq 8$

    (f) $x - 6 \leq -3$

    (g) $x + 8 \leq 5$

    (h) $\dfrac{x}{2} \geq 3$

    (i) $\dfrac{x}{4} \leq -1$

4. Solve each of the following inequalities and illustrate your solutions on a number line.

    (a) $6x + 2 \geq 8$

    (b) $5x - 3 > 7$

    (c) $3x - 9 < 6$

    (d) $4x + 2 \leq 30$

    (e) $5x + 9 \leq -1$

    (f) $4x + 12 > 4$

    (g) $\dfrac{x}{2} + 4 > 3$

    (h) $\dfrac{x}{5} - 1 \leq -3$

    (i) $\dfrac{x}{4} + 6 \leq 5$

5. Solve the following inequalities, illustrating your solutions on a number line.

    (a) $-1 \leq 3x + 2 \leq 17$

    (b) $4 - 6x < 22$

    (c) $5 - 3x \geq -1$

    (d) $14 \leq 4x - 2 \leq 18$

    (e) $20 - 8x < 4$

    (f) $32 - 9x \geq -4$

    (g) $11 - 3x \leq 20$

    (h) $-11 \leq 3x - 2 \leq -5$

    (i) $-7 < 2x + 5 \leq 1$

6.   Given that the perimeter of the
      rectangle shown is less than 44,
      form and solve an inequality.

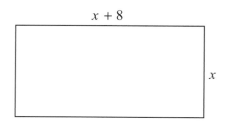

7.   The perimeter of the triangle shown
      is greater than 21 but less than or
      equal to 30.

      Form and solve an inequality
      using this information.

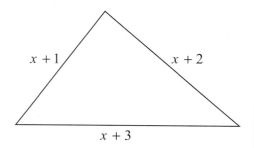

8.   The area of the rectangle shown
      must be less than 50 but greater
      than or equal to 10.

      Form and solve an inequality for x.

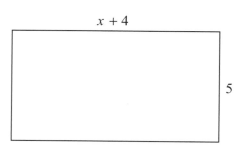

9.   A cyclist travels at a constant speed v miles per hour. He travels 30 miles
      in a time that is greater than 3 hours but less than 5 hours.
      Form an inequality for v.

10.   The area of a circle must be greater than or equal to 10 m^2 and less than
      20 m^2. Determine an inequality that the radius, r, of the circle must satisfy.

11.   The pattern shown is formed by
      straight lines of equations in the
      first quadrant.

      (a)   One region of the pattern
            can be described by the
            inequalities

                  $x \leq 2$

                  $x \geq 1$

                  $y \geq x$

                  $y \leq 3$

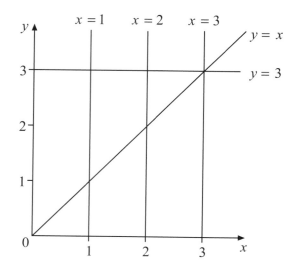

      Copy the diagram and put an R in the single region of the pattern that
      is described.

This is another pattern formed by straight line graphs of equations in the first quadrant.

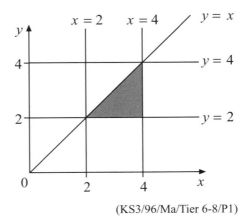

(b)   The shaded region can be described by *three* inequalities.

Write down these three inequalities.

(KS3/96/Ma/Tier 6-8/P1)

13.2 Graphs of Quadratic Functions

In this section we recap the graphs of straight lines before looking at the graphs of quadratic functions.

> A straight line has equation $y = mx + c$ where m is the gradient and c is the y-intercept.

Example 1

(a)   Draw the lines with equations,

$$y = x + 8 \qquad \text{and} \qquad y = x + 3.$$

(b)   Describe the translation that would move $y = x + 8$ onto $y = x + 3$.

Solution

(a)   To plot the graphs, we calculate the coordinates of three points on each line.

For $y = x + 8$ we have

$$(-3, 5), \quad (0, 8) \quad \text{and} \quad (4, 12).$$

For $y = x + 3$ we have,

$$(-4, -1), \quad (0, 3) \quad \text{and} \quad (3, 6).$$

The graphs are shown below.

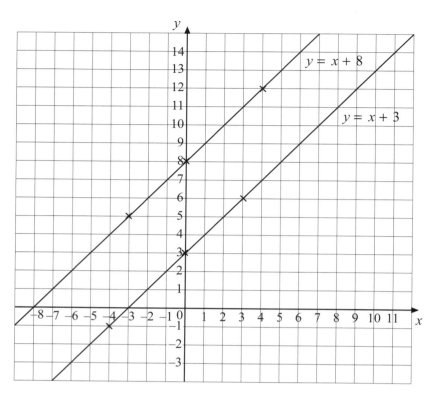

(b)   A translation along the vector $\begin{pmatrix} 0 \\ -5 \end{pmatrix}$ would move the line $y = x + 8$ onto the line $y = x + 3$.

Example 2

Draw the curve with equation $y = x^2$.

Solution

$y = x^2$ is not a linear equation, so we will have to draw a smooth curve. To do this we need to calculate and plot a reasonable number of points. We begin by drawing up a table of values:

x	-3	-2	-1	0	1	2	3
x^2	9	4	1	0	1	4	9

Using these values the graph can be drawn, as shown:

$y = x^2$

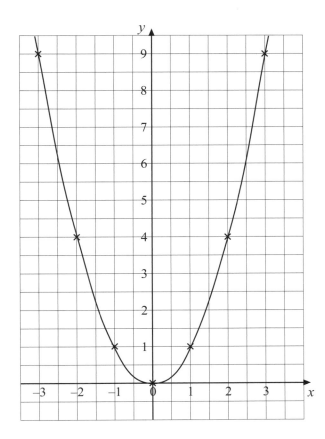

Example 3

(a) Draw the curve with equation $y = x^2 + 2$.

(b) Describe how the curve is related to the curve with equation $y = x^2$.

Solution

(a) A table of values has been completed:

x	-3	-2	-1	0	1	2	3
$x^2 + 2$	11	6	3	2	3	6	11

The graph is shown below:

$y = x^2 + 2$

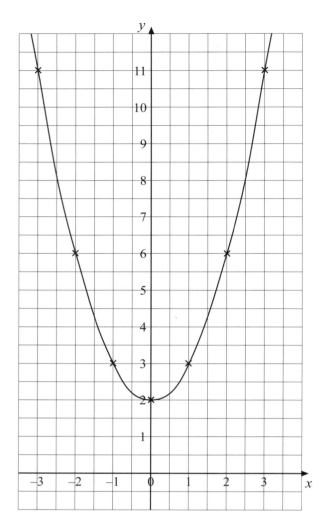

(b)   This curve is a translation of the curve $y = x^2$ along the vector $\begin{pmatrix} 0 \\ 2 \end{pmatrix}$.

Exercises

1.   (a)   Draw the graph with equation $y = 2x + 1$.

      (b)   State the gradient of this line.

2.   Draw the line that has gradient $-\dfrac{1}{2}$ and y-intercept 6.

3.   (a)   Draw the lines with equations $y = 2x + 3$ and $y = -2x + 3$.

      (b)   Describe the transformation that would map one line onto the other.

4.   (a)   Draw the curves with equations $y = x^2$ and $y = x^2 - 1$.

      (b)   Describe how the two curves are related.

5. (a) Draw the curves with equations $y = x^2 + 3$ and $y = x^2 - 1$.

    (b) Describe the transformation that would map the first curve onto the second.

6. Without drawing any graphs, describe the relationship between the curves with equations,

    $$y = x^2 + 1, \qquad y = x^2 - 5 \quad \text{and} \quad y = x^2 + 6.$$

7. (a) Copy and complete the following table:

x	-4	-3	-2	-1	0	1	2	3	4
$x^2 + 2x$									

    (b) Draw the graph $y = x^2 + 2x$.

    (c) Describe how this curve is related to the curve with equation $y = x^2$.

8. (a) Draw the curve $y = 2x^2$.

    (b) On the same diagram, also draw the curves with equations $y = 2x^2 - 1$ and $y = 2x^2 + 2$.

    (c) Describe how the three curves are related.

9. (a) Draw the graphs with equations $y = x^2 + 4$ and $y = 2 - x^2$.

    (b) Describe the transformation that would map one curve onto the other.

10. (a) Draw the curves with equations $y = x^2 - 4x$ and $y = x^2 + 2x + 3$.

    (b) Describe the relationship between the two curves.

11. (a) The diagram shows the graph with equation $y = x^2$.

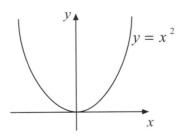

    Copy the diagram and, on the same axes, sketch the graph with equation $y = 2x^2$.

(b)   Curve A is the reflection in the x-axis of $y = x^2$.

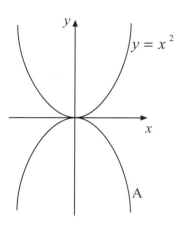

What is the equation of curve A ?

(c)   Curve B is the translation, one unit up the y-axis, of $y = x^2$.

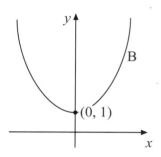

What is the equation of curve B ?

(d)   The shaded region is bounded by the curve $y = x^2$ and the line $y = 2$.

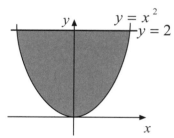

Write down *two* of the inequalities below which together *fully describe* the shaded region.

$$y < x^2 \qquad x < 0 \qquad y < 2 \qquad y < 0$$
$$y > x^2 \qquad x > 0 \qquad y > 2 \qquad y > 0$$

(KS3/98/Ma/Tier 6-8/P1)

13.3 Graphs of Cubic and Reciprocal Functions

In this section we look at the graphs of cubic functions, i.e. the graphs of functions whose polynomial equations contain x^3 and no higher powers of x. We also look at the graphs of reciprocal functions, for example, $y = \frac{1}{2}x$, $y = \frac{3}{x}$ and $y = \frac{-2}{x}$.

Example 1

(a)   Draw the graph of $y = x^3$.

(b)   Describe the symmetry of the curve.

Solution

(a)   First complete a table of values:

x	-3	-2	-1	0	1	2	3
$y = x^3$	-27	-8	-1	0	1	8	27

The graph is shown below:

(b) $y = x^3$

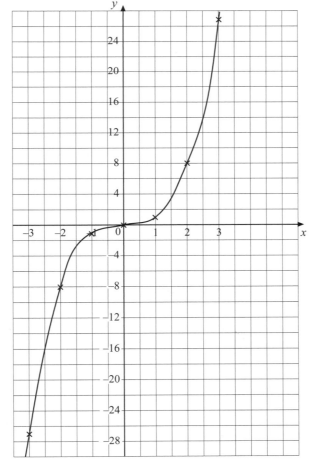

(b)   The graph has rotational symmetry of order 2 about the point with coordinates $(0, 0)$.

Example 2

Draw the graph with equation $y = x^3 - 3x$.

Solution

Completing a table of values gives:

x	-4	-3	-2	-1	0	1	2	3	4
$y = x^3 - 3x$	-52	-18	-2	2	0	-2	2	18	52

The graph is shown below:

$y = x^3 - 3x$

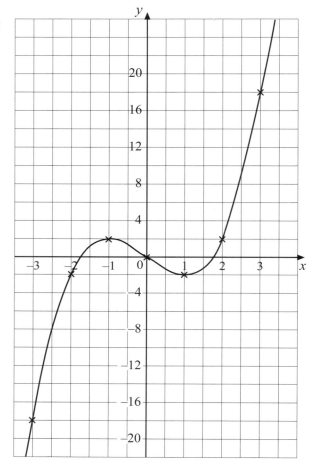

Example 3

(a) Draw the curve with equation $y = \dfrac{8}{x}$.

(b) On the same diagram, draw the line with equation $y = x + 2$.

(c) Write down the coordinates of the points where the line crosses the curve.

Solution

(a) Completing a table of values gives:

x	-8	-4	-2	-1	$-\frac{1}{2}$	$\frac{1}{2}$	1	2	4	8
$y = \dfrac{8}{x}$	-1	-2	-4	-8	-16	16	8	4	2	1

Note that $\dfrac{8}{x}$ is not defined when $x = 0$.

These values can then be used to draw the graph below.

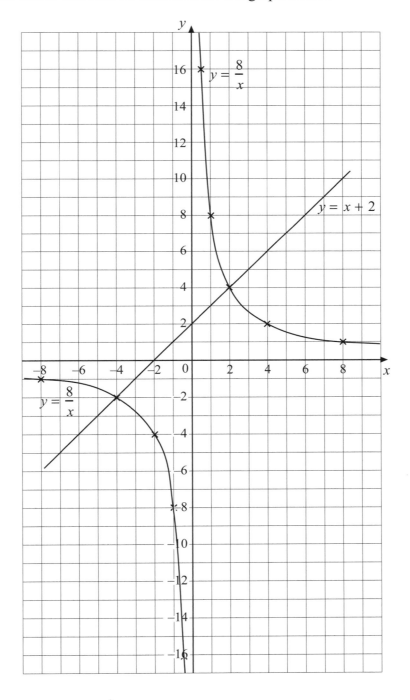

(b)   The line $y = x + 2$, which passes through $(-6, -4)$, $(0, 2)$ and $(8, 10)$. has been added to the graph above.

(c)   The coordinates of these points are $(-4, -2)$ and $(2, 4)$.

Exercises

1.   (a)   On the same set of axes, draw the graphs with equations,
$$y = x^3 + 5, \qquad y = x^3 - 1 \qquad \text{and} \qquad y = x^3 - 4.$$

      (b)   Describe how the graphs are related.

2.   (a)   Draw the graph of the curve with equation $y = x^3 - x$.

      (b)   Describe the symmetry of the curve.

3.   (a)   Draw the graph of the curve with equation $y = (x+1)^3$.

      (b)   Describe how the curve relates to the graph of $y = x^3$.

      (c)   Describe the symmetry of the curve $y = (x+1)^3$.

4.   (a)   Draw the graph of the curve with equation $y = (x-2)^3$.

      (b)   Describe the symmetry of this curve.

5.   (a)   Draw the graphs of the curves with equations $y = 2 - x^3$ and $y = x^3$.

      (b)   Describe the transformation that would map one curve onto the other.

6.   (a)   Copy and complete the following table:

x	-4	-2	-1	$-\frac{1}{2}$	$\frac{1}{2}$	1	2	4
$\frac{1}{x}$								

      (b)   Use these values to draw the graph of the curve with equation $y = \dfrac{1}{x}$.

      (c)   Describe the symmetry of this curve.

7. On the same set of axes, draw the curves with equations,

$$y = \frac{1}{x}, \qquad y = \frac{2}{x} \quad \text{and} \quad y = \frac{4}{x}.$$

8. (a) On the same set of axes, draw the curve with equation $y = \frac{6}{x}$ and the line with equation $y = 7 - x$, for values of x from $\frac{1}{2}$ to 7.

   (b) Write down the coordinates of the points where the line intersects the curve.

9. Determine, by drawing a graph, the coordinates of the points where the line with equation $y = x - 3$ intersects the curve with equation $y = \frac{10}{x}$. Use values of x from -4 to 6.

10. Determine, graphically, the coordinates of the points where the curve $y = \frac{1}{x}$ intersects the curves with equations,

    (a) $y = x^2$, \qquad\qquad (b) $y = x^3$.

13.4 Solving Non-Linear Equations

In this section we consider how to solve equations by using graphs, trial and improvement or a combination of both.

Example 1

Solve the equation $x^3 + x = 6$ by using a graph.

Solution

The graph $y = x^3 + x$ should be drawn first, as shown.

A line can then be drawn on the graph from 6 on the y-axis, across to the curve and down to the x-axis. This gives an approximate solution between 1.6 and 1.7, so graphically we might estimate x to be 1.65.

$y = x^3 + x$

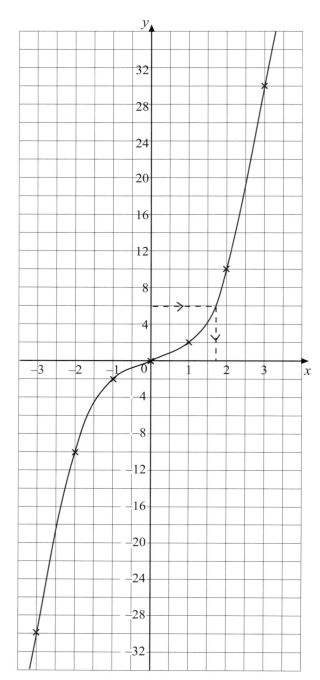

Example 2

Determine a solution to the equation $x^3 + x = 6$ correct to 2 decimal places.

Solution

The previous example suggested graphically that there is a solution of the equation between $x = 1.6$ and $x = 1.7$. We will now use a trial and improvement method to find x to 2 decimal places, using $x = 1.6$ as a starting value in the process.

Trial x	$x^3 + x$	Comment
1.6	5.696	$1.6 < x$
1.7	6.613	$1.6 < x < 1.7$
1.65	6.142125	$1.6 < x < 1.65$
1.63	5.960747	$1.63 < x < 1.65$
1.64	6.050944	$1.63 < x < 1.64$
1.635	6.00572288	$1.63 < x < 1.635$

At this stage we can conclude that the solution is $x = 1.63$ correct to 2 decimal places.

Example 3

Use a graph and trial and improvement to solve the equation $x^3 + x^2 = 10$.

Solution

The graph indicates that there will be a solution that is a little less than 2, approximately 1.9.

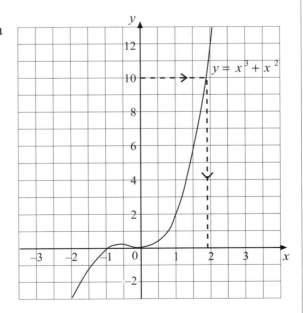

A trial and improvement approach is now used to determine x to a greater degree of accuracy.

Trial x	$x^3 + x^2$	Comment
1.9	10.469	$x < 1.9$
1.8	9.072	$1.8 < x < 1.9$
1.85	9.754125	$1.85 < x < 1.9$
1.88	10.179072	$1.85 < x < 1.88$
1.87	10.036103	$1.85 < x < 1.87$
1.86	9.894456	$1.86 < x < 1.87$
1.865	9.96511463	$1.865 < x < 1.87$

The solution is $x = 1.87$ correct to 2 decimal places.

Note: The equation $x^3 + x^2 = 10$ had just one solution. However, in general, there may be more than one solution. For example, the diagram shows that the equation $x^3 + x^2 = 0.1$ has three solutions.

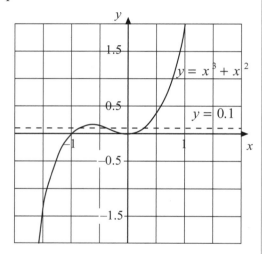

Exercises

1. Use a graph to determine the 2 solutions to the equation $x^2 + x = 6$.

2. (a) Draw the graph $y = 2x^2 - x$.

   (b) Use the graph to determine approximate solutions to the equations:

      (i) $2x^2 - x = 8$,

      (ii) $2x^2 - x = 5$.

3. The following graph is for $y = x^3 - x^2 - 6x$.

   Use the graph to solve the following equations:

   (a) $x^3 - x^2 - 6x = 8$ (b) $x^3 - x^2 - 6x = -10$

   (c) $x^3 - x^2 - 6x = 2$ (d) $x^3 - x^2 - 6x = -4$

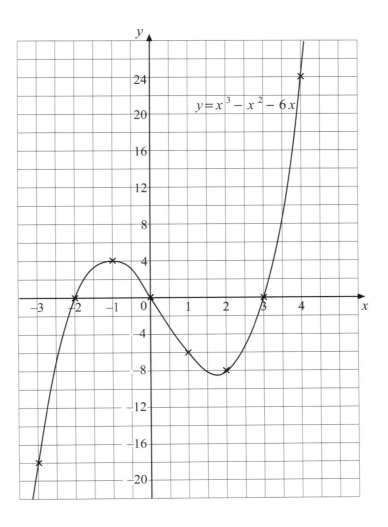

4. The equation $x^3 + x = 1000$ has a solution close to $x = 10$.

    Use trial and improvement to obtain the solution correct to 2 decimal places.

5. The equation $x + \sqrt{x} = 5$ has a solution between $x = 3$ and $x = 4$. Find this solution correct to 2 decimal places.

6. Use a graphical method followed by trial and improvement to determine both solutions of the equation $x^2 + 6x = 8$, correct to 2 decimal places.

7. The equation $x + \dfrac{1}{x} = 8$ has 2 solutions.

    (a) Use a graph to determine approximates values for these solutions.

    (b) Determine these solutions correct to 2 decimal places using trial and improvement.

8. The equation $8x^2 - x^3 = 5$ has 3 solutions. Determine each solution correct to 1 decimal place.

9. The equation $\dfrac{1}{x} + x^2 = 1$ has 1 solution. Determine this solution correct to 2 decimal places.

10. Determine each of the solutions of the equation $x^3 - 4x = 2$ correct to 2 decimal places.

11. The table below shows values of x and y for the equation $y = x^2 + x - 5$.

    (a) Copy and complete the table.

x	-2	-1	0	1	2	3
y				-3	1	7

    The value of y is 0 for a value of x between 1 and 2.

    (b) Find the value of x, to 1 decimal place, that gives the value of y closest to 0.

    You may use trial and improvement, as shown.

x	y
1	-3
2	1

    (KS3/96/Ma/Tier 6-8/P1)

12. Enid wants to find the roots of the equation $2x^2 = 10x - 5$.
    The roots are the values of x which make the equation correct.

    Enid works out values of $2x^2$ and $10x - 5$.
    She also works out the difference between each pair of values by subtracting the value $10x - 5$ from the value of $2x^2$.
    Enid notes whether this difference is positive or negative.

x	$2x^2$	$10x - 5$	Difference	
-2	8	-25	$+33$	Positive
-1	2	-15	$+17$	Positive
0	0	-5	$+5$	Positive
1	2	5	-3	Negative
2	8	15	-7	Negative

    (a) One root of the equation $2x^2 = 10x - 5$ lies between $x = 0$ and $x = 1$.
    Use the table to explain why.

Enid then tries *1 decimal place* numbers for *x*.

x	$2x^2$	$10x - 5$	Difference
0.3	0.18	-2	$+2.18$
0.4	0.32	-1	$+1.32$
0.5	0.50	0	$+0.50$
0.6	0.72	1	-0.28
0.7	0.98	2	-1.02

(b) Between which two *1 decimal place* numbers does the root lie?

(c) Try some *2 decimal place* numbers for *x*.
Show all your trials in a table like the one below.

Find the two values of *x* between which the root lies.

Write down *all the digits* you get for the values of $2x^2$, $10x - 5$ and Difference.

x	$2x^2$	$10x - 5$	Difference

(d) Between which two *2 decimal place* numbers does the root lie?

(KS3/95/Ma/Levels 5-7/P1)

13.

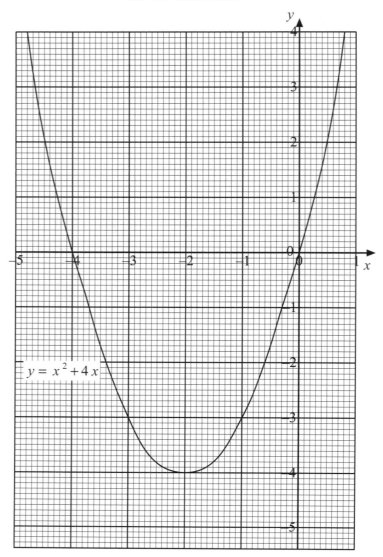

The graph shows $y = x^2 + 4x$.

(a) Solve the equation $x^2 + 4x - 2 = 0$ using the graph.
     Give your answers to 2 decimal places.

(b) Give an example of another equation you could solve in a similar way
     using the graph.

(c) The equation $x^2 + 4x + 5 = 0$ cannot be solved using the graph.
     Why not?

Kelly used an iterative method to find a more accurate solution to the
equation $x^2 + 4x - 2 = 0$.

Kelly's method was $x_{n+1} = \dfrac{2}{x_n + 4}$

(d) Explain how Kelly's method relates to the equation $x^2 + 4x - 2 = 0$.

Kelly started with $x_1 = 1$ used her iterative method four times. She got these results.

x_1	x_2	x_3	x_4	x_5
1	0 4	0.4545455	0.4489796	0.4495413

(e) Steve used a different iterative method.

Steve's method was $x_{n+1} = \dfrac{2 - 4x_n}{x_n}$.

He started with $x_1 = 1$.

Work out x_2, x_3, x_4 and x_5 and write them showing all the digits on your calculator.

(KS3/95/Ma/Levels 9-10)

13.5 Quadratic Inequalities

In the first section of this unit we considered *linear inequalities*. In this section we will consider *quadratic inequalities* and make use of both graphs and the factorisation that you used in Unit 11.

We begin with a graphical approach.

Example 1

(a) Draw the graph $y = x^2 + 3x - 10$.

(b) Use the graph to solve the inequality $x^2 + 3x - 10 \geq 0$.

Solution

The graph is shown below. Note that $x^2 + 3x - 10 = 0$ at $x = -5$ and $x = 2$.

The graph shows that

$$x^2 + 3x - 10 \geq 0$$

when $x \leq -5$ or $x \geq 2$.

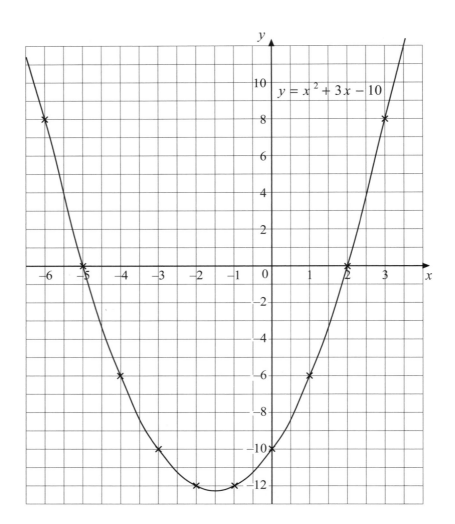

 ## Example 2

Solve the inequality

$$x^2 - 6x < 0$$

 ## Solution

Factorising gives:

$$x^2 - 6x = x(x - 6)$$

So $x^2 - 6x = 0$ when $x = 0$ or $x = 6$.

Sketching the graph as shown
indicates that the solution is

$$0 < x < 6.$$

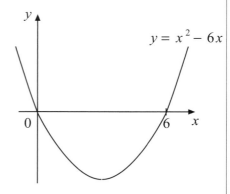

 ## Example 3

Solve the inequality

$$25 - x^2 > 0$$

Solution

Factorising gives:

$$25 - x^2 = (5 - x)(5 + x)$$

So $25 - x^2 = 0$ when $x = 5$ or $x = -5$.

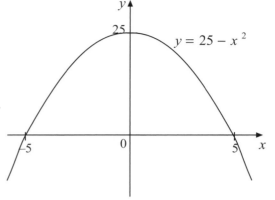

The sketch shows that $25 - x^2 > 0$
will be satisfied when $-5 < x < 5$.

Exercises

1. (a) Draw the graph $y = x^2 + 2x - 3$.

   (b) Solve the inequality $x^2 + 2x - 3 \geq 0$

   (c) Solve the inequality $x^2 + 2x - 3 < 0$.

2. Use a graph to solve the inequality $1 - x^2 < 0$.

3. Use a graph to solve the inequality $x^2 + 3x - 4 \leq 0$.

4. (a) Factorise $x^2 - 5x$.

   (b) Sketch the graph of $y = x^2 - 5x$.

   (c) State the solution of the inequality $x^2 - 5x < 0$.

5. Solve the following inequalities:
   (a) $x^2 + 5x > 0$ (b) $x^2 - 3x \leq 0$

   (c) $x - x^2 < 0$ (d) $2x - x^2 \geq 0$

6. (a) Factorise $x^2 - 49$.

   (b) Sketch the graph of $y = x^2 - 49$.

   (c) State the solution of the inequality $x^2 - 49 > 0$.

7. Solve the inequalities:

    (a) $x^2 - 36 < 0$

    (b) $100 - x^2 \geq 0$

    (c) $x^2 - 16 \leq 0$

    (d) $81 - x^2 < 0$

8. (a) Factorise $x^2 - 5x - 14$.

    (b) Sketch the graph of $y = x^2 - 5x - 14$.

    (c) State the solution of the inequality $x^2 - 5x - 14 \geq 0$.

9. Solve the inequalities:

    (a) $x^2 - 6x - 27 < 0$

    (b) $x^2 + 7x + 12 \leq 0$

    (c) $x^2 - 13x + 40 > 0$

    (d) $x^2 - 7x - 18 \geq 0$

10. (a) Factorise $-x^2 + 12x - 27$.

    (b) Sketch the graph of $y = -x^2 + 12x - 27$.

    (c) State the solution of the inequality $x^2 - 12x + 27 < 0$.

11. Denise and Luke are using the expression $\dfrac{n(n+1)}{2}$ to generate triangular numbers.

    For example, the triangular number for $n = 4$ is $\dfrac{4(4+1)}{2}$, which works out to be 10.

    (a) Denise wants to solve the inequality $300 < \dfrac{n(n+1)}{2} < 360$ to find the two triangular numbers between 300 and 360.

    What are these two triangular numbers?

    You may use trial and improvement.

    (b) Luke wants to find the two smallest triangular numbers which fit the inequality $\dfrac{n(n+1)}{2} > 2700$.

    What are these two triangular numbers?

    You may use trial and improvement.

    (KS3/95/Ma/Tier 6-8/P1)

13.6 Equations of Perpendicular Lines

In this section we consider the relationship between perpendicular lines.

> If one line has gradient m, $m \neq 0$, a line that is
>
> perpendicular to it will have gradient $\dfrac{-1}{m}$.

Note: The examples that follow make use of the general equation $y = mx + c$ for a straight line with gradient m and y-intercept c.

Example 1

A line passes through the origin and is perpendicular to the line with equation $y = 7 - x$. Determine the equation of the line.

Solution

The line's equation $y = 7 - x$ can be rewritten in the form $y = -x + 7$ showing that it has gradient -1.

A perpendicular line will have gradient $\dfrac{-1}{-1} = 1$ and so its equation will be $y = x + c$.

As it passes through the origin, we know $y = 0$ when $x = 0$.

Substituting these values into the equation gives,

$$0 \ = \ 0 + c$$

so

$$c \ = \ 0$$

Hence the equation is $y = x$.

Example 2

A line passes through the points with coordinates $(2, 6)$ and $(5, -1)$.
A second line passes through the points with coordinates $(0, 3)$ and $(7, 6)$.
Are the two lines perpendicular?

Solution

Gradient of first line $= \dfrac{(-1) - 6}{5 - 2}$

$= \dfrac{-7}{3}$

Gradient of second line $= \dfrac{6 - 3}{7 - 0}$.

$= \dfrac{3}{7}$.

But as $\dfrac{3}{7} = \dfrac{-1}{\left(\dfrac{-7}{3}\right)}$, the lines are perpendicular.

Note: This example illustrates an alternative way of looking at the relationship between the gradients of perpendicular lines, namely that the product of their gradients is -1.

For example, $\dfrac{-7}{3} \times \dfrac{3}{7} = -1$

Exercises

1.   (a)   Draw the line with equation $y = 2x - 1$.

   (b)   Determine the equation of a perpendicular line that passes through the origin.

   (c)   Draw this line and check that it is perpendicular.

2.   The equations of 5 lines are given below.

   A $y = 8x - 5$

   B $y = 3x + 2$

   C $y = -\dfrac{2x}{16} + 1$

   D $y = 4 - \dfrac{x}{3}$

   E $y = \dfrac{-x}{8} + 7$

   Which line or lines are:

   (a)   perpendicular to A,   (b)   perpendicular to B ?

3.   The points A, B, C and D have coordinates $(1, 3)$, $(6, 1)$, $(3, 1)$ and $(5, 6)$ respectively. Show that AB is perpendicular to CD.

4.   A quadrilateral has corners at the points with coordinates $Q\,(7, 3)$, $R\,(6, 5)$, $S\,(2, 3)$ and $T\,(3, 1)$.

   Show that QRST is a rectangle.

5.   The line with equation $y = 7 - x$ and a perpendicular line intersect at the point with coordinates $(4, 3)$. Determine the equation of the perpendicular line.

6. Are the lines with equations

$$y = \frac{x-2}{3} \text{ and } y = 8 - 3x$$

perpendicular?

7. A line passes through the origin and the point $(4, 7)$. Determine the equations of the perpendicular lines that pass through:

(a) the origin,   (b) the point $(4, 7)$.

8. A line is drawn perpendicular to the line $y = \frac{1}{2}x + 4$ so that it passes through the point with coordinates $(3, 3)$.

(a) Determine the equation of the perpendicular line.

(b) Determine the coordinates of the point where the two lines intersect.

9. Two perpendicular lines intersect at the point with coordinates $(4, 6)$. One line has gradient -4. Determine the equations of the two lines

10. Two perpendicular lines intersect at the point with coordinates $(6, 5)$. One line passes through the origin. Where does the other line intersect the x-axis?

14 Estimation and Approximation

14.1 Rounding

There are three main ways to round numbers:

(i)   to the *nearest* 10, 100, 1000, etc;

(ii) to a certain number of *significant figures*;

(iii) to a certain number of *decimal places*.

Note that a measured length such as '12 cm to the nearest cm' means that the actual length lies between 11.5 cm and 12.5 cm.

By convention, we normally round 0.5 up to the next whole number, so in fact,

$$11.5 \text{ cm} \leq \text{actual length} < 12.5 \text{ cm}$$

We call 11.5 the *lower bound* and 12.5 the *upper bound*. We can also write the upper bound as

$$12.4999 \ldots \ldots \text{ or } 12.4\dot{9}$$

where the dot above the 9 means that it is repeated indefinitely, or recurs.

It is important to see that 12.49 is *not* the upper bound, as, for example, the length could have been 12.498.

 ## Example 1

A football match is watched by 56 742 people. Write this number correct to the nearest,

(a)   10 000,   (b)   1000,   (c)   10.

 ### Solution

(a)   56 742 = 60 000 to the nearest 10 000.

(b)   56 742 = 57 000 to the nearest 1000.

(c)   56 742 = 56 740 to the nearest 10.

 ## Example 2

Write each of the following numbers correct to 3 significant figures:

(a)   47 316   (b)   303 971

(c)   20.453   (d)   0.004368

 ### Solution

(a)   47 316   = 47 300 to 3 significant figures.

(b)   303 971   = 304 000 to 3 significant figures.

(c)   20.453   = 20.5 to 3 significant figures.

(d)   0.004368 = 0.00437 to 3 significant figures.

Example 3

Write each of the following numbers correct to the number of decimal places stated:

(a)   0.3741   to   2 d.p.

(b)   3.8451   to   2 d.p.

(c)   142.8315   to   1 d.p.

(d)   0.000851   to   4 d.p.

Solution

(a)   0.3741   =   0.37   to 2 decimal places.

(b)   3.8451   =   3.85   to 2 decimal places

(c)   142.8315 =   142.8   to 1 decimal place.

(d)   0.000851 =   0.0009   to 4 decimal places.

Example 4

State the upper and lower bounds for each of the following quantities and write an inequality for the actual value in each case.

(a)   4 mm to the nearest mm.

(b)   15 kg to the nearest kg.

(c)   4.56 m to the nearest cm.

Solution

(a)   Upper bound = 4.5 mm
       Lower bound = 3.5 mm $3.5 \text{ mm} \le \text{actual value} < 4.5 \text{ mm}$

(b)   Upper bound = 15.5 kg
       Lower bound = 14.5 kg $14.5 \text{ kg} \le \text{actual value} < 15.5 \text{ kg}$

(c)   Upper bound = 4.565 m
       Lower bound = 4.555 m $4.555 \text{ m} \le \text{actual value} < 4.565 \text{ m}$

Exercises

1. Round each of the following numbers to the nearest 100:

   (a) 108   (b) 199   (c) 3471

   (d) 59   (e) 33   (f) 451

2. Round the number 4 765 173 to:

   (a) the nearest million,   (b) the nearest 10,

   (c) the nearest 1000,   (d) the nearest 100.

3. Write each of the following numbers correct to 3 significant figures:

   (a) 37 412   (b) 84 563   (c) 261.42

   (d) 0.3684   (e) 0.002615   (f) 0.0025713

   (g) 3.6213   (h) 4.0071   (i) 18.3071

4. Write each of the following numbers correct to 2 decimal places:

   (a) 7.431   (b) 8.269   (c) 4.7135

   (d) 11.925   (e) 24.8603   (f) 44.0019

5. Write each of the following numbers correct to the number of significant figures stated:

   (a) 6.475 to 2 s.f.   (b) 1473 to 1 s.f.

   (c) 3681 to 2 s.f.   (d) 571.32 to 4 s.f.

   (e) 16 001 to 3 s.f.   (f) 148.25 to 3 s.f.

   (g) 16.999 to 3 s.f.   (h) 38.9712 to 2 s.f.

   (i) 160.37 to 4 s.f.

6. Write the number 183.9591 correct to:

   (a) 3 decimal places   (b) 3 significant figures

   (c) 2 significant figures   (d) 5 significant figures

   (e) 1 decimal place   (f) 1 significant figure

7. Barry rounds the number 374.49 to 375.

   (a) Explain what mistake he has made.

   (b) Describe how Barry tried to round the number and then give the correct answer.

8. Use a calculator to carry out the following calculations. In each case, give the answer correct to 2 significant figures.

    (a) $33 \div 4$ (b) $22 \div 0.7$ (c) $142 \div 0.8$

    (d) 66×1.27 (e) 3.25×1001 (f) 62×47

    (g) 3.41×0.0092 (h) $88 \div 0.007$ (i) 42×1.0952

9. The mass of a ship is stated as 47 384 tonnes to the nearest tonne. Are the following statements correct?

    (a)   The mass is *less* than 47 384.5 tonnes.

    (b)   The mass is *greater* than 47 384.4 tonnes.

10. Annie says that her rabbit has a mass of 1473 grams. Give this mass correct to:

    (a)   the nearest 100 grams,

    (b)   the nearest 10 grams,

    (c)   the nearest kg.

11. At an athletics meeting, the discus throws are measured to the nearest centimetre.

    (a)   Viv's best throw was measured as 35.42 m.

    Could Viv's throw actually have been more than 35.42 m ?

    Explain your answer.

    (b)   Chris won the hurdles race in a time of 14.6 seconds measured to the nearest tenth of a second.

    Between what two values does Chris's time actually lie?

    (KS3/95/Ma/Levels 5-7/P1)

12. The table shows the lengths of some rivers to the nearest km.

    (a)   (i)   Write the length of each river rounded to the nearest 100 km.

River	Length in km to the nearest km	Length in km to the nearest 100 km
Severn	354	
Thames	346	
Trent	297	
Wye	215	
Dee	113	

    (ii)   Which two rivers have the *same length* to the nearest 100 km?

(b)   (i)   Write the length of each river rounded to the nearest 10 km.

River	Length in km to the nearest km	Length in km to the nearest 10 km
Severn	354	
Thames	346	
Trent	297	
Wye	215	
Dee	113	

(ii)   Which two rivers have the *same length* to the nearest 10 km?

(c)   There is another river which is not on the list.

It has a length of 200 km to the nearest 100 km, and a length of 150 km to the nearest 10 km.

Copy and complete this sentence to give one possible length of the river to the nearest km.

The length of the river could be .... km.

(d)   Two more rivers have different lengths to the nearest km.

They both have a length of 250 km to the nearest 10 km, but their lengths to the *nearest 100 km* are *different*.

Copy and complete this sentence to give a possible length of each river to the nearest km.

The lengths of the rivers could be .... km and .... km.

(KS3/98/Ma/Tier 4-6/P2)

13. (a)   The length of an envelope is 21 cm to the nearest cm.

What is the smallest possible real length of the envelope?

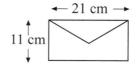

(b)   The interval on the number line below shows all the possible real lengths of the envelope.

Write down the correct numbers for the lower and upper limits of the interval, represented on the diagram by A and B.

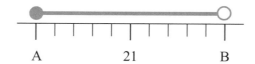

A   21   B

(c)   The length of a card is 20.5 cm to the nearest tenth of a cm.

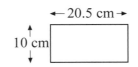

The interval on the number line below shows all the possible real lengths of the card.

Write down the numbers represented on the number line by C, D and E.

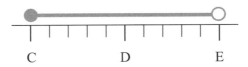

(d)   Can you be sure the card will fit in the open envelope like this?

Explain why.

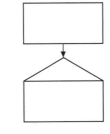

(KS3/94/Ma/5-7/P2)

14.2 Estimation

Estimation is important because it allows you to check that the answers you obtain on a calculator are reasonable. It is easy to make a simple mistake when using a calculator or working out a problem by hand, so an estimation of the expected answer is a useful check.

One of the simplest approaches to estimation is to round all the numbers involved to 1 significant figure.

Example 1

(a)   Estimate the value of 4.73×18.4.

(b)   Use a calculator to find 4.73×18.4.

(c)   Compare the estimate with the exact value.

Solution

(a) $4.73 \times 18.4 \approx 5 \times 20 = 100$

(b) $4.73 \times 18.4 = 87.032$

(c)   Because in (a) we rounded both numbers up, the estimate is slightly bigger than the actual value, but it does give us an idea of the size of the answer.

Example 2

The correct answer to 14.1×18.3 is listed below, along with 3 incorrect answers.

25.803

258.03

2580.3

25803

Use estimation to decide which is the correct answer.

Solution

$14.1 \times 18.3 \approx 10 \times 20 = 200$

So the correct answer must be 258.03

Although we often round to 1 significant figure, we can sometimes produce better estimates by using other values that are still easy to work with. For example, in Example 2 above, we could have said that

$$14.1 \times 18.3 \approx 14 \times 20 = 280$$

which is closer to the correct answer 258.03

The important thing to remember is that you must be able to do the estimation calculation *in your head*.

Example 3

Estimate the value of:

(a) $\sqrt{\dfrac{3.87 \times 14.6}{9.32}}$

(b) $\sqrt{\dfrac{72 \times 33.4}{41}}$

Solution

(a) $\sqrt{\dfrac{3.87 \times 14.6}{9.32}} \approx \sqrt{\dfrac{4 \times 10}{10}} = \sqrt{4} = 2$

or

$\sqrt{\dfrac{3.87 \times 14.6}{9.32}} \approx \sqrt{\dfrac{4 \times 16}{9}} = \dfrac{2 \times 4}{3} = \dfrac{8}{3} = 2\dfrac{2}{3} = 2.\dot{6}$

Note that the actual value is 2.462 to 3 d.p.

(b) $\sqrt{\dfrac{72 \times 33.4}{41}} \approx \sqrt{\dfrac{70 \times 30}{40}} = \sqrt{\dfrac{2100}{40}} = \sqrt{\dfrac{2000}{40}} = \sqrt{50}$

Note that $\sqrt{50}$ is between 7 and 8, but will be closer to 7 since $7 = \sqrt{49}$. We can therefore take 7 as our estimate.

The actual value is 7.659 to 3 d.p.

You might also need to approximate when converting between different units. The following list reminds you of some of the important approximations between metric and imperial units.

8 km	$\approx$	5 miles
1 m	$\approx$	40 inches
30 cm	$\approx$	1 foot
2.5 cm	$\approx$	1 inch
1 kg	$\approx$	2.2 lbs
1 litre	$\approx$	$1\dfrac{3}{4}$ pints
1 gallon	$\approx$	$4\dfrac{1}{2}$ litres
1 acre	$\approx$	$\dfrac{2}{5}$ hectare
450 g	$\approx$	1 lb

Exercises

1. Estimate the answer to each of the following calculations:

    (a) 3.6×14.3

    (b) 47×192

    (c) 33.6×403

    (d) 11.25×76.3

    (e) 12.84×3.94

    (f) $103.6 \div 21.72$

    (g) $44.32 \div 1.987$

    (h) $68.39 \div 7.48$

    (i) $12.021 \div 5.917$

2. Estimate the value of each of the following:

    (a) $\sqrt{\dfrac{3.9 \times 17.45}{4.23}}$

    (b) $\sqrt{8.1^2 + 7.32^2}$

    (c) $\sqrt{\dfrac{62.4 \times 18.3}{4.7}}$

    (d) $\sqrt{\dfrac{11.42 \times 19.99}{3.851}}$

3.   James writes down this statement:

$$14.62 \times 401 = 586.262$$

   (a)   Use estimation to describe why James must be wrong.

   (b)   Use a calculator to determine the correct answer, and then describe the mistake that James made.

4.   Use estimation to decide which of the following calculations are definitely incorrect:

   (a) $15.2 \times 6120 = 930\,240$ (b) $65.224 \div 12.4 = 5.26$

   (c) $192 \times 4587 = 880\,704$ (d) $346.92 \div 2.36 = 14.7$

5.   For each of the following calculations three possible answers are given, but only one is correct. Use estimation to select the correct answer.

   (a) $3.712 \times 805 = \begin{cases} 298.816 \\ 2988.16 \\ 298881.6 \end{cases}$

   (b) $2955.82 \div 9.82 = \begin{cases} 301 \\ 3010 \\ 30100 \end{cases}$

   (c) $\sqrt{\dfrac{7.2^2 + 8.1^2}{4}} = \begin{cases} 541.87 \\ 54.187 \\ 5.4187 \end{cases}$

   (d) $\dfrac{84.2 + 73.6}{2.2} = \begin{cases} 71.73 \\ 7.173 \\ 0.7173 \end{cases}$

6.   The month of December has 31 days. Estimate the number of seconds in December. Compare your estimate with the correct value.

7.   Estimate the circumference of a circle with a radius of 20.5 cm.

8.   A book has 326 pages with an average of 268.4 words on each page. Estimate the number of words in the book.

9.   At a school the average daily amount spent by each child in the canteen is £1.42. There are 1264 pupils in the school. Estimate the total amount spent in the canteen each day.

10. Estimate the area of a circle of radius 6.27 cm.

11. Carl has an old recipe for egg custard with raisins.

    (a) The custard must be cooked at 320 degrees Fahrenheit.
        Carl has a rule to change the temperature to degrees Celsius.

        Rule:

        To change the temperature to degrees Celsius,

        subtract 32 from the temperature in degrees Fahrenheit,

        then multiply the answer by 5,

        then divide by 9.

        Use Carl's rule to change 320 degrees Fahrenheit to degrees Celsius.
        You must show each step in your calculation.

    (b) Carl is using this recipe:

        Egg Custard with Raisins

        $\frac{1}{4}$ pound of raisins

        1 pint of milk

        3 eggs

        Put the raisins in an 8 inch bowl.

        Mix the eggs and milk, and pour over the raisins.
        Bake in the oven at 320 ° Fahrenheit for about an hour.

        He starts to change the amounts into *metric* measures.

        Write down the words or numbers missing from the sentences below.

        Egg Custard with Raisins

        About 100 grams of raisins

        About 0.5 .... of milk

        3 eggs

        Put the raisins in a .... centimetre bowl.

(KS3/96/Ma/Tier 4-6/P1)

14.3 Calculator Use

In this section we consider how to make the best use of calculators. We focus on the use of *brackets*. We will then look at the use of the *memory* functions. Calculators vary a great deal both in the number of memories available and in how they are used. It is essential for you to learn how *your* calculator memory works.

Example 1

Calculate $\dfrac{4.7 + 3.2}{8.6 - 3.1}$, giving your answer to 3 decimal places.

Solution

Use the following keys to obtain the correct answer:

(4 . 7 + 3 . 2) ÷

(8 . 6 − 3 . 1) =

You should obtain 1.436363636, which rounds to 1.436 to 3 decimal places.

Note how brackets have been used around both the numerator and the denominator of the fraction.

Example 2

Zarah uses her calculator to obtain an answer to,

$$\frac{4.7}{102 - 3.8}$$

She obtains the answer -3.75 to 2 decimal places.

(a) Use estimation to show that her answer is incorrect.

(b) Describe the error she made when using her calculator, and write down the calculation that she actually carried out.

(c) Calculate the correct answer, correct to 3 significant figures.

Solution

(a) $\dfrac{4.7}{102 - 3.8} \approx \dfrac{5}{100 - 4} \approx \dfrac{5}{100} = 0.05$

The estimate indicates that Zarah's negative answer must be incorrect.

(b) Zarah forgot to include brackets around the denominator of the fraction. She actually calculated

$$\frac{4.7}{100} - 3.8$$

(c)   The correct answer can be obtained by using the following sequence of keys:

$$4 \quad \cdot \quad 7 \quad \div \quad (\quad 1 \quad 0 \quad 2 \quad - \quad 3 \quad \cdot \quad 8 \quad) \quad =$$

This gives a value of 0.047861507, which is 0.0479 to 3 significant figures.

Note that this compares well with the estimate.

Exercises

1.   Calculate the answers to the following, giving your answers to 2 significant figures:

(a) $\dfrac{3.8 \times 4.7}{6.2 + 8.9}$ (b) $\dfrac{42.3}{8.6 + 12.9}$

(c) $\dfrac{56.7 - 8}{3.2}$ (d) $\dfrac{11.4 + 19.6}{7.31}$

(e) $\dfrac{4.87 + 3.62}{5.9 - 0.62}$ (f) $\dfrac{14.6}{8.2} - \dfrac{3.7}{4.9}$

(g) $\dfrac{4.3 \times 3.07 \times 6.109}{2.9 \times 9.81 \times 5.006}$ (h) $\dfrac{21 \times (3 - 2.1)}{4.7 + 12.8}$

2.   Calculate the following, giving your answers correct to 3 significant figures:

(a) $(6.72 - 3.8)^2$ (b) $(4.62 + 3.84)^3$

(c) $\sqrt{6.2 + 7.4}$ (d) $(3.68 + 2.41) \times (8.21 - 3)$

(e) $6.2^2 \times (14.2 - 8.03)$ (f) $11.4^2 + (3.8 - 4.2)^2$

3.   For each calculation below, first obtain an estimate of the answer and then calculate the actual answer, where necessary rounding the value to 3 significant figures.

(a) $\dfrac{81.4}{12 - 3.2}$ (b) $\dfrac{33.6}{4.52} - \dfrac{11.2}{21.5}$

(c) $\dfrac{88.92 - 14.37}{2.69}$ (d) $\dfrac{84.3 + 18.92}{3(4.6 - 0.17)}$

4.   Joseph and Jenny use their calculators to try to calculate,

$$\frac{3.7 + 8.9}{4.61}$$

When they round to 3 significant figures, Joseph obtains the answer 5.63 and Jenny gets 2.73.

(a)   Use estimation to decide who has the *incorrect* answer.

(b)   Describe the calculation that was used to obtain the *incorrect* answer.

(c)   Check that the other answer is *correct*.

5.   Dee and Daniella press the keys on their calculators in the following sequences:

Dee

Daniella

(a)   What answers do they obtain?

(b)   Write down the calculation that Dee has the answer to.

(c)   Write down the calculation that Daniella has the answer to.

6.   Adrian calculates the number of seconds in 2 hours and 40 minutes as 2520. His brother, Richard, says that he is wrong and that the correct answer is 9600 seconds.

(a)   Use an estimate to show that Adrian must be wrong.

(b)   Write down the calculations that the brothers did to obtain their answers.

7.   Denise says that she can obtain the answer to

$$\frac{3.6}{17.2} + \frac{8.6}{3.5}$$

using her calculator, but without using brackets. Hannah disagrees. Who is correct? Explain why.

8.   Which of the following can be calculated on a calculator, without using brackets or a memory?

(a) $3 \times 7 + 8 \times 32$ (b) $\dfrac{4}{9} + \dfrac{6}{25}$

(c) $\dfrac{11 + 6}{4}$ (d) $\dfrac{3 \times 2}{4}$

(e) $\dfrac{5 \times 2}{8 \times 3}$ (f) $\dfrac{22 + 1}{5}$

9. For each of the following calculations, first obtain an estimate and then calculate the actual value, where necessary giving your answer correct to 3 significant figures.

(a) $\sqrt{\dfrac{3.7}{0.84}}$

(b) $\sqrt{\dfrac{8.2}{1.6}} + \sqrt{\dfrac{9.2}{1.3}}$

(c) $\sqrt{8.4^2 + 4.8^2 - 2 \times 8.4 \times 4.8}$

(d) $\dfrac{\sqrt{82} - \sqrt{63}}{\sqrt{47} \times \sqrt{32}}$

10. (a) Write down the sum that you would use to calculate the number of seconds in 3 days, 4 hours and $28\frac{1}{2}$ minutes.

(b) Obtain the answer on your calculator.

11. David is studying blood cells through a microscope.

The diameter of a red cell is 0.000714 cm and the diameter of a white cell is 0.001243 cm.

(a) Use a calculator to work out the difference between the diameter of a red cell and the diameter of a white cell.

Give your answer in *millimetres*.

David wants to explain how small the cells are.
He calculates how many white cells would fit across a full stop which has a diameter of 0.65 mm.

(b) How many whole white cells would fit across the full stop?

(KS3/95/Ma/Levels 5-7/P1)

12. Rectangles with length and width in the special ratio $1 : \dfrac{2}{1 + \sqrt{5}}$ are called golden rectangles.

Some artists use them because the proportions look attractive.

(a) Work out $\dfrac{2}{1 + \sqrt{5}}$.

Write this using all the decimal places your calculator shows.

(b) Ramesh used his calculator efficiently to work out $\dfrac{2}{1 + \sqrt{5}}$.

He did *not* have to write down any numbers and then key them back into his calculator.

Show the steps he might have used with his calculator.

(c)   Four faces of this cuboid are golden rectangles.

The volume of the cuboid is:

$$\left(\frac{2}{1+\sqrt{5}}\right) \times \left(\frac{2}{1+\sqrt{5}}\right) \times 1$$

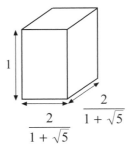

Use a *short* and *accurate* method on your calculator to calculate this. Write the volume using all the decimal places your calculator shows.

(d)   Show the steps you used to make your method *short* and *accurate*.

(KS3/94/Ma/5-7/P1)

14.4 Error Propagation

If there is an error in a value that is used in a calculation, that error can become more significant when the calculation is made. For example, if the radius of a circle is rounded from 2.57 cm to 2.6 cm, an error of 0.49 cm^2 would be made when calculating the area of the circle.

In this section we consider how errors introduced by rounding can be increased (or *propagated*) in subsequent calculations.

Example 1

The radius of a circle is given as 31 cm, correct to the nearest cm. What are the possible errors when calculating its area?

Solution

As the radius, *r* cm, is given as 31 cm to the nearest cm, we have

$$30.5 \le r < 31.5$$

If $r = 30.5$, $A = \pi \times 30.5^2$

                              $= 2922.466566$ cm^2

                              $= 2920$ cm^2 to 3 s.f.

If $r = 31$, $A = \pi \times 31^2$

                              $= 3019.07054$ cm^2

                              $= 3020$ cm^2 to 3 s.f.

If $r = 31.5$, $A = \pi \times 31.5^2$

                              $= 3117.245311$ cm^2

                              $= 3120$ cm^2 to 3 s.f.

If $r = 30.5$, then the error is

$$3019.07054 - 2922.466566 = 96.603974 \text{ cm}^2$$

whilst, if $r = 31.5$, the error is

$$3117.245311 - 3019.07054 = 98.17477043 \text{ cm}^2$$

Hence the maximum possible error occurs when $r = 31.5$, and is approximately 98.2 cm^2. In other words, there is a potential error here of almost 100 cm^2 in the area if we calculate it from the rounded radius.

Example 2

A rectangular plot of land has sides with lengths of 38 m and 52 m correct to the nearest m.

Calculate the maximum and minimum possible values of:

(a)   the *perimeter* of the rectangle,

(b)   the *area* of the rectangle.

52 m

38 m

Solution

(a)   The sides have been given to the nearest metre, so

$$51.5 \text{ m} \le \text{length} < 52.5 \text{ m}$$

$$37.5 \text{ m} \le \text{width} < 38.5 \text{ m}$$

$$\begin{aligned} \text{Minimum perimeter} &= 2(37.5 + 51.5) \\ &= 178 \text{ m} \end{aligned}$$

$$\begin{aligned} \text{Maximum perimeter} &= 2(38.5 + 52.5) \\ &= 182 \text{ m} \end{aligned}$$

(b) $\begin{aligned} \text{Minimum area} &= 37.5 \times 51.5 \\ &= 1931.25 \text{ m}^2 \end{aligned}$

$\begin{aligned} \text{Maximum area} &= 38.5 \times 52.5 \\ &= 2021.25 \text{ m}^2 \end{aligned}$

Example 3

The values of x and y are given to 1 decimal place as $x = 4.2$ and $y = 7.3$

Determine the minimum and maximum values of:

(a) $x + y$ (b) $y - x$ (c) $\dfrac{x}{y}$

Solution

First note that $4.15 \le x < 4.25$ and $7.25 \le y < 7.35$.

(a)   Minimum value of $x + y = 4.15 + 7.25$ (minimum value of x

$= 11.4$ + minimum value of y)

Maximum value of $x + y$ = $4.25 + 7.35$ (maximum value of y
                                                    + maximum value of x)
                        = 11.6

(b)   Minimum value of $y - x$ = $7.25 - 4.25$ (minimum value of y
                                                    − maximum value of x)
                            = 3

      Maximum value of $y - x$ = $7.35 - 4.15$ (maximum value of y
                                                    − minimum value of x)
                            = 3.2

(c)   Minimum value of $\dfrac{x}{y}$ = $\dfrac{4.15}{7.35}$ = 0.56462585 (minimum value of x
                                                                    ÷ maximum value of y)
                            = 0.565 to 3 s.f.

      Maximum value of $\dfrac{x}{y}$ = $\dfrac{4.25}{7.25}$ = 0.586206896 (maximum value of x
                                                                    ÷ minimum value of y)
                            = 0.586 to 3 s.f.

Note that, for x and y both positive,

To find *maximum* value of $x + y$ or xy,
    use the largest value of x and largest value of y.

To find the *minimum* value of $x + y$ or xy,
    use the smallest value of x and smallest value of y.

To find *maximum* value of $x - y$ or $\dfrac{x}{y}$,
    use the largest value of x and smallest value of y.

To find the *minimum* value of $x - y$ or $\dfrac{x}{y}$,
    use the smallest value of x and largest value of y.

Exercises

1.   A car park is a square with sides of length 48 m correct to the nearest metre.
     Calculate the maximum and minimum possible values for:

     (a)   the *perimeter* of the car park,   (b)   the *area* of the car park.

2.   The radius of a circle is given as 9 cm correct to the nearest cm. Calculate the
     maximum and minimum possible values for the area of the circle. Round
     your upper and lower bounds to 2 decimal places.

3.	A rectangle has sides of length 1.27 m and 2.43 m correct to 2 decimal places. Calculate the maximum and minimum possible values for:

(a)	the *perimeter,*	(b)	the *area.*

4.	The formula $V = \dfrac{4\pi r^3}{3}$ is used to calculate the volume of a sphere of radius r. A sphere has radius 18 cm correct to the nearest cm.

Calculate the maximum and minimum possible values for the volume of the sphere. Round your upper and lower bounds to 2 decimal places.

5.	If x and y are given correct to 1 decimal place as $x = 5.2$ and $y = 11.6$, calculate the maximum and minimum possible values of:

(a)	x^2		(b)	$x + y$		(c)	xy

(d)	$y - x$		(e)	$x^2 + y^2$		(f)	$\dfrac{x}{y}$

6.	Hannah measures with a ruler that has marks every 0.5 cm. She says that the lengths of the side of a rectangle are 8.5 cm and 12 cm correct to the nearest 0.5 cm.

Calculate the minimum possible values of:

(a)	the *perimeter* of the rectangle,

(b)	the *area* of the rectangle.

7.	The radius of a circle is said to be 18 m ± 0.5 m.

(a)	What is the *maximum* possible radius of the circle?

(b)	Write the *circumference* of the circle in the form a m ± b m, giving the values of a and b correct to 2 decimal places.

8.	A square has sides with lengths that are given as 1.8 cm ± 0.05 cm.

(a)	Write the *perimeter* of the square in the form a cm ± b cm.

(b)	Write the *area* of the square in the form a cm^2 ± b cm^2.

9.	The area of a square is given as 14 m^2 correct to the nearest m^2. Calculate the maximum and minimum possible values for the length of the side of the square, rounding your answers to 3 significant figures.

10.	A circle has area 50 cm^2 ± 2 cm^2 What are the maximum and minimum possible values of the radius of the circle? Round your upper and lower bounds to 2 decimal places.

11. Mary, Arvind and Nesta wrote a mass to different numbers of decimal places.

Mary wrote 1.7 to 1 decimal place.
Arvind wrote 1.748 to 3 decimal places.

(a) Can both of them be correct?
Explain how you decided.

(b) Nesta wrote 1.7474 to 4 decimal places.

Can both Nesta and Arvind be correct?
Explain how you decided.

(c) They wrote a volume to different numbers of decimal places.

Mary wrote 2.6 to 1 decimal place.
Arvind wrote 2.65 to 2 decimal places.

They are both correct.

What are the lower and upper bounds of the volume?

(d) The mass of a block is 0.10 kilograms to 2 decimal places.

Its volume is 0.02 litres to 2 decimal places.

$$\text{density} = \frac{\text{mass}}{\text{volume}}$$

Work out the minimum and maximum possible density of the block.

Show your working.

(e) The maximum possible percentage error in the density of the block can be thought of in different ways and therefore calculated using different methods.

Investigate two different methods which give a maximum percentage error greater than 30%.

Calculate the values they give for the percentage error.

Show your working.

(KS3/94/Ma/9-10/Ext)

12. The exact formula to convert a temperature measured in degrees Celsius (C) to degrees Fahrenheit (F) is

$$F = \frac{9C}{5} + 32$$

An approximate formula often used for this conversion is

$$F = 2C + 30$$

(a)   The temperature is 20.0 °C, measured to the nearest tenth of a degree. What would you obtain as the upper and lower bounds of the temperature in degrees Fahrenheit if you used the approximate formula for the conversion?

(b)   What are the upper and lower bounds of the temperature in degrees Fahrenheit obtained by using the exact formula to convert 20.0 °C to Fahrenheit?

(c)   Calculate the percentage error when the approximate formula, rather than the exact formula, is used to convert 30.0 °C to Fahrenheit.

(d)   For what range of values of C does the approximate formula give an answer in degrees Fahrenheit which differs by a percentage error of no more than 5% from the exact formula?

Give your answers to one decimal place.

(KS3/95/Ma/Levels 9-10)

15 Trigonometry

15.1 Pythagoras' Theorem

Pythagoras' Theorem describes the important relationship between the lengths of the sides of a right-angled triangle.

Pythagoras' Theorem

In a right-angled triangle,

$$a^2 + b^2 = c^2$$

The longest side, *c*, in a right-angled triangle is called the *hypotenuse*.

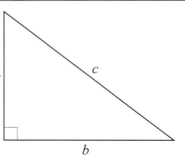

Example 1

Calculate the length of the side AB of this triangle:

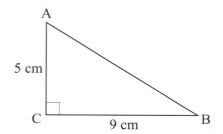

Solution

In this triangle,

$$AB^2 = AC^2 + BC^2$$
$$= 5^2 + 9^2$$
$$= 25 + 81$$
$$= 106$$

$$AB = \sqrt{106} = 10.29563014 \text{ cm}$$
$$= 10.3 \text{ cm} \quad (\text{to 1 decimal place})$$

Example 2

Calculate the length of the side XY of this triangle.

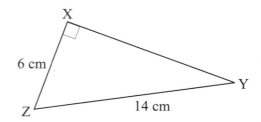

Solution

In this triangle,

$$YZ^2 = XY^2 + XZ^2$$

$$14^2 = XY^2 + 6^2$$

$$196 = XY^2 + 36$$

$$XY^2 = 160$$

$$XY = \sqrt{160} = 12.64911064 \text{ cm}$$

$$= 12.6 \text{ cm} \quad \text{(to 1 decimal place)}$$

Example 3

Determine whether or not this triangle contains a right angle.

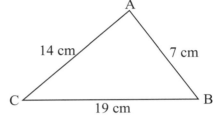

Solution

If the triangle does contain a right angle, then the longest side, BC, would be the hypotenuse. So, the triangle will be right-angled if $AB^2 + AC^2 = BC^2$.

First consider,

$$AB^2 + AC^2 = 7^2 + 14^2 = 49 + 196$$

$$= 245$$

Now consider,

$$BC^2 = 19^2$$

$$= 361$$

In this triangle,

$$AB^2 + AC^2 \neq BC^2$$

so it does *not* contain a right angle.

Exercises

1. Calculate the length of the hypotenuse of each of the triangles shown. Where necessary, give your answers correct to 2 decimal places.

(a)

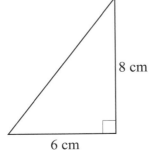

(b)

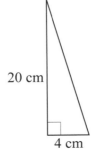

(c)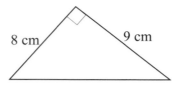

(d)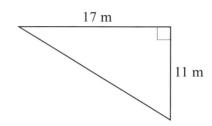

2. Calculate the length of the unmarked side of each of the triangles shown. In each case, give your answer correct to 2 decimal places.

(a)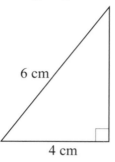

(b)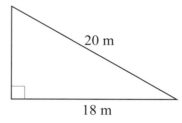

(c)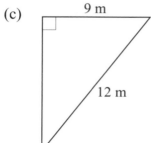

(d)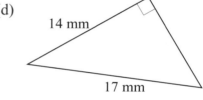

3. (a) Determine AB.

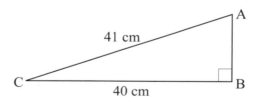

(b) Determine EF.

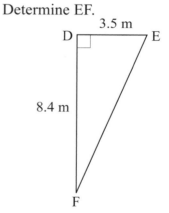

(c) Determine GH.

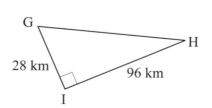

(d) Determine JK.

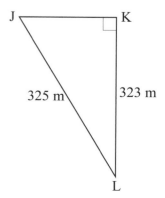

4. Which of the triangles below contain right angles?

(a)

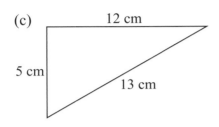

10 cm   6 cm

8 cm

(b)

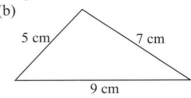

5 cm   7 cm

9 cm

(c)

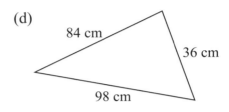

12 cm

5 cm

13 cm

(d)

84 cm   36 cm

98 cm

5. Sam walks 100 m north and then 100 m east. How far is she from her starting position? Give your answer to a sensible degree of accuracy.

6. Calculate the perimeter of the trapezium shown. Give your answer to the nearest millimetre.

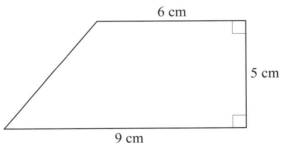

6 cm

5 cm

9 cm

7. The diagram shows a plan for a wheelchair ramp.

The distance AC is 2 m.

Giving your answer in metres, correct to the nearest cm, calculate the distance AB if:

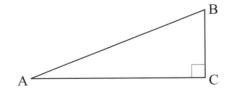

A   B   C

(a) BC = 20 cm   (b) BC = 30 cm

8. Calculate the perimeter and area of this trapezium:

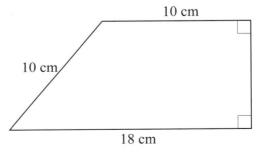

10 cm

10 cm

18 cm

9. A rope is 10 m long. One end is tied to the top of a flagpole. The height of the flagpole is 5 m. The rope is pulled tight with the other end on the ground.

   How far is the end of the rope from the base of the flagpole? Give your answer to a sensible level of accuracy.

10. A ladder leans against a vertical wall. The length of the ladder is 5 m. The foot of the ladder is 2 m from the base of the wall.

    How high is the top of the ladder above the ground?
    Give your answer to a sensible level of accuracy.

11. Sarah makes a kite from two isosceles triangles, as shown in the diagram.

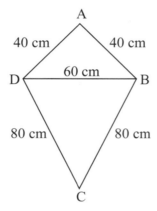

    Calculate the height, AC, of the kite, giving your answer to the nearest centimetre.

12. *In this question you will get* no marks *if you work out the answer through scale drawing.*

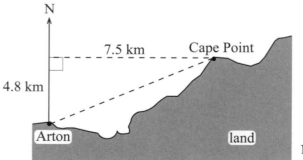

    Cape Point is 7.5 km east and 4.8 km north of Arton.

    Calculate the direct distance from Arton to Cape Point.
    Show your working.

(KS3/98/Ma/Tier 5-7/P2)

13. A cupboard needs to be strengthened by putting a strut on the back of it like this.

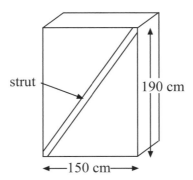

(a) Calculate the length of the diagonal strut.
     Show your working.

(b) In a small room the cupboard is in this position.

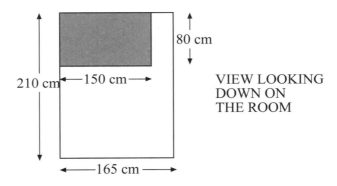

     VIEW LOOKING
     DOWN ON
     THE ROOM

     Calculate if the room is wide enough to turn the cupboard like this and put it in its new position.

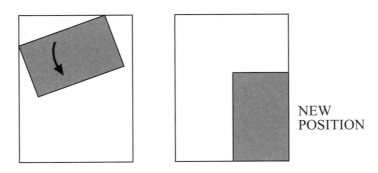

     NEW
     POSITION

     Show your working.

     (KS3/95/Ma/Levels 5-7/P1)

15.2 Trigonometric Functions

In this section we introduce 3 functions: *sine, cosine* and *tangent,* and their use in right-angled triangles. First we look at the conventions used for the names of the sides of a right-angled triangle with respect to one of the angles.

The *adjacent* side is the side joining the angle and the right angle.

The *opposite* side is opposite the angle.

The *hypotenuse* is the side opposite the right angle and is the longest side in the triangle.

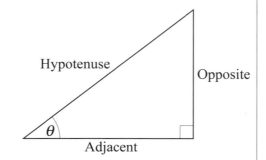

Using these definitions, we can write down the trigonometric functions:

$$\sin\theta \;=\; \frac{\text{opposite}}{\text{hypotenuse}} \;=\; \frac{O}{H}$$

$$\cos\theta \;=\; \frac{\text{adjacent}}{\text{hypotenuse}} \;=\; \frac{A}{H}$$

$$\tan\theta \;=\; \frac{\text{opposite}}{\text{adjacent}} \;=\; \frac{O}{A}$$

Note that we abbreviate sine, cosine and tangent to sin, cos and tan.

In the following Examples and Exercises, we investigate the properties of these trigonometric functions.

Example 1

Estimate the sin, cos and tan of 30 °, using an accurate drawing of the triangle shown.

Solution

The triangle has been drawn accurately below, and the sides measured.

Here, hypotenuse $= 11.6$ cm , adjacent $= 10$ cm and opposite $= 5.8$ cm, so,

$$\sin 30° \ = \ \frac{O}{H} \ = \ \frac{5.8}{11.6} \ = \ 0.5$$

$$\cos 30° \ = \ \frac{A}{H} \ = \ \frac{10}{11.6} \ = \ 0.86 \ \text{(to 2 decimal places)}$$

$$\tan 30° \ = \ \frac{O}{A} \ = \ \frac{5.8}{10} \ = \ 0.58$$

Note that if we had drawn a similar right-angled triangle, again containing the 30 ° angle but with different side lengths, then we may have obtained slightly different values for $\sin 30°$, $\cos 30°$ and $\tan 30°$. You can obtain more accurate values of $\sin 30°$, $\cos 30°$ and $\tan 30°$ by using a scientific calculator. If you have a calculator with the trigonometric functions, do this and compare them with the values above.

WARNING: When you use a scientific calculator, always check that it is dealing with angles *in degree mode.*

Example 2

(a)   Measure the angle marked in the following triangle:

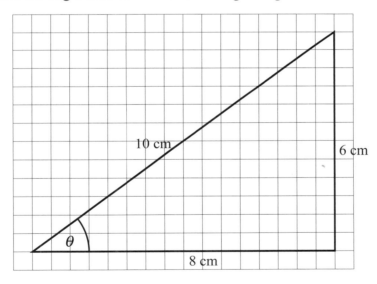

(b)   Calculate the sine, cosine and tangent of this angle.

Solution

(a)   In this case the angle can be measured with a protractor as 37 °.

(b)   Here we have

$$\text{opposite } = 6 \text{ cm}$$

$$\text{adjacent } = 8 \text{ cm}$$

$$\text{hypotenuse } = 10 \text{ cm}$$

$$\sin\theta = \frac{O}{H} \qquad \cos\theta = \frac{A}{H} \qquad \tan\theta = \frac{O}{A}$$

$$= \frac{6}{10} \qquad\qquad = \frac{8}{10} \qquad\qquad = \frac{6}{8}$$

$$= 0.6 \qquad\qquad\quad = 0.8 \qquad\qquad\quad = 0.75$$

Exercises

1. (a) Draw 3 different right-angled triangles that each contain a 60 ° angle.

   (b) Use each triangle to estimate sin 60 °, and check that you get approximately the same value in each case.

   (c) Estimate a value for cos 60 °.

   (d) Estimate a value for tan 60 °.

2. (a) Draw a right-angled triangle that contains an angle of 50 °.

   (b) Use this triangle to estimate:

       (i)   cos 50 °,   (ii)   sin 50 °,   (iii)   tan 50 °.

3. (a) Draw a right-angled triangle which contains a 45 ° angle.

   (b) Explain why sin 45 ° = cos 45 ° and state the value of tan 45 °.

4. (a) Copy and complete the following table, giving your values correct to 2 significant figures.

   Draw appropriate right-angled triangles to be able to estimate the values.

Angle	sine	cosine	tangent
10 °			
20 °			
30 °			
40 °			
50 °			
60 °			
70 °			
80 °			

   (b) Use the sin, cos and tan keys on your calculator to check your values.

5.   A pupil states that the sine of an angle is 0.5. What is the angle?

6.   If the cosine of an angle is 0.17, what is the angle? Give the most accurate answer you can obtain from your calculator and then round it to the nearest degree.

7.   What are the values of:

(a) $\cos 0°$ (b) $\sin 0°$ (c) $\sin 90°$

(d) $\cos 90°$ (e) $\tan 0°$ (f) $\tan 90°$

8.   Use your calculator to obtain the following, correct to 3 significant figures:

(a) $\sin 82°$ (b) $\cos 11°$ (c) $\sin 42°$

(d) $\tan 80°$ (e) $\tan 52°$ (f) $\tan 38°$

9.   Use your calculator to obtain the angle θ, correct to 1 decimal place, if:

(a) $\cos \theta = 0.3$ (b) $\sin \theta = 0.77$ (c) $\tan \theta = 1.62$

(d) $\sin \theta = 0.31$ (e) $\cos \theta = 0.89$ (f) $\tan \theta = 11.4$

10.   A student calculates that $\cos \theta = 0.8$.

(a)   By considering the sides of a suitable right-angled triangle, determine the values of $\sin \theta$ and $\tan \theta$.

(b)   Use a calculator to find the angle θ.

(c)   Use the angle you found in part (b) to verify your answers to part (a).

15.3 Calculating Sides

In this section we use the trigonometric functions to calculate the lengths of sides in a right-angled triangle.

Trigonometric Functions		
$\sin \theta = \dfrac{O}{H}$	$\cos \theta = \dfrac{A}{H}$	$\tan \theta = \dfrac{O}{A}$

Example 1

Calculate the length of the side marked x in this triangle.

Solution

In this question we use the *opposite* side and the *hypotenuse*. These two sides appear in the formula for $\sin\theta$, so we begin with,

$$\sin\theta = \frac{O}{H}$$

In this case this gives,

$$\sin 40° = \frac{x}{8}$$

or

$$x = 8 \times \sin 40°$$
$$= 5.142300877 \text{ cm}$$
$$= 5.1 \text{ cm to 1 decimal place}$$

Example 2

Calculate the length of the side AB of this triangle.

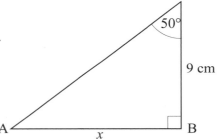

Solution

In this case, we are concerned with side A B which is the *opposite* side and side BC which is the *adjacent* side, so we use the formula,

$$\tan\theta = \frac{O}{A}$$

For this problem we have,

$$\tan 50° = \frac{x}{9}$$

so $$x = 9 \times \tan 50°$$
$$= 10.72578233 \text{ cm}$$
$$= 10.7 \text{ cm to 1 decimal place}$$

Example 3

Calculate the length of the hypotenuse of
this triangle.

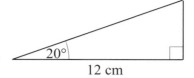

Solution

In this case, we require the formula that links the *adjacent* side and the *hypotenuse,*
so we use $\cos\theta$.

Starting with

$$\cos\theta = \frac{O}{H}$$

we can use the values from the triangle to obtain,

$$\cos 20° = \frac{12}{H}$$

$$H \times \cos 20° = 12$$

$$H = \frac{12}{\cos 20°}$$

$$= 12.77013327 \text{ cm}$$

Therefore the hypotenuse has length 12.8 cm to 1 decimal place.

Exercises

1. Use the formula for the sine to determine the length of the side marked x in
    each of the following triangles. In each case, give your answer correct to 1
    decimal place.

    (a)

    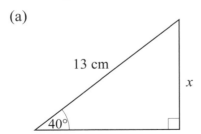

    (b)

    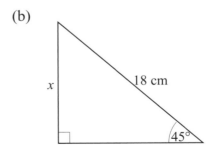

    (c)

    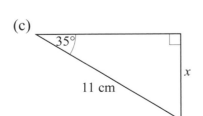

    (d)

    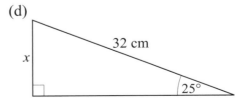

2.   Use the formula for the cosine to determine the length of the *adjacent* side in each of the following triangles. Give your answers correct to 1 decimal place.

(a)

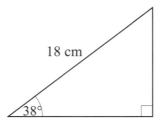

(b)

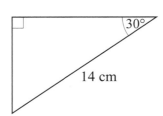

(c)

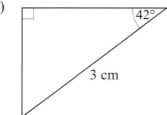

(d)

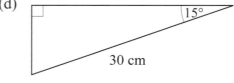

3.   Calculate the length of sides indicated by letters in each of the following triangles. Give each of your answers correct to 3 significant figures.

(a)

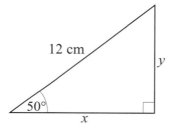

(b)

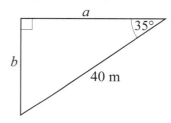

(c)

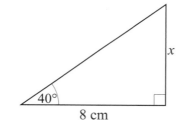

(d)

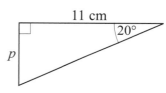

(e)

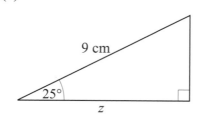

(f)

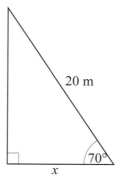

4. Calculate the length of the *hypotenuse* of each of the following triangles. Give each of your answers correct to 3 significant figures.

    (a)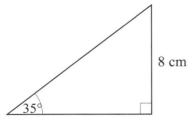

    (b)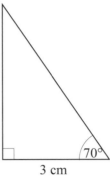

    (c)

    (d)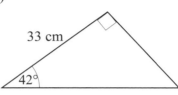

5. Calculate all the lengths marked with letters in the following triangles. Give each of your answers correct to 2 decimal places.

    (a)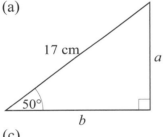

    (b)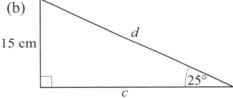

    (c)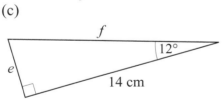

    (d)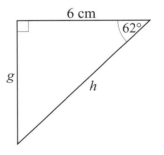

6. A ladder, which has length 6 m, leans against a vertical wall. The angle between the ladder and the horizontal ground is 65 °.

    (a)   How far is the foot of the ladder from the wall?

    (b)   What is the height of the top of the ladder above the ground?

    In each case, give your answer to the nearest centimetre.

7. A boat sails 50 km on a bearing of 070 °.

    (a)   How far *east* does the boat travel?

    (b)   How far *north* does the boat travel?

    In each case, give your answer to a sensible level of accuracy.

8. Calculate the *perimeter* and *area* of
    this triangle. Give your answers
    correct to 2 decimal places.

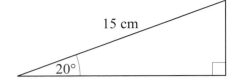

15 cm

20°

9. A ramp has length 6 m and is at an angle of 50 ° above the horizontal. How
    high is the top of the ramp? Give your answer to a sensible level of
    accuracy.

10. A rope is stretched from a window in the side of a building to a point on the
    ground, 6 m from the base of the building. The angle between the rope and
    the side of the building is 19 °.

    (a)   How long is the rope?

    (b)   How high is the window?

    In each case, give your answer correct to the nearest centimetre.

15.4 Calculating Angles

In this section we use trigonometry to determine the sizes of angles in right-
angled triangles. On your scientific calculator you will find buttons labelled
'$\sin^{-1}$', '$\cos^{-1}$' and '$\tan^{-1}$'. You will need to be able to use these to calculate
the angles that will arise in the problems which follow. Again, we start with the
three trigonometric functions:

$$\boxed{\begin{array}{c} \textit{Trigonometric Functions} \\[4pt] \sin\theta = \dfrac{O}{H} \qquad \cos\theta = \dfrac{A}{H} \qquad \tan\theta = \dfrac{O}{A} \end{array}}$$

Example 1

Calculate the angle θ in this triangle.

Solution

In this triangle we are given the lengths of the
adjacent and opposite sides, so we will use,

$$\tan\theta = \frac{O}{A}$$

Using the lengths given, we have

$$\tan\theta \;=\; \frac{8}{5}$$

$$=\; 1.6$$

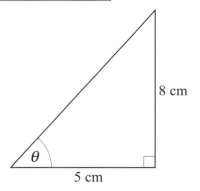

8 cm

θ

5 cm

We can then use the $\tan^{-1}$ key on a calculator to obtain

$$\theta = \tan^{-1}(1.6) = 57.99461678°$$

$$= 58.0° \quad \text{(to 1 decimal place)}$$

Example 2

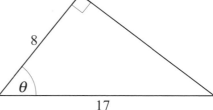

Calculate the angle marked θ in this triangle.

Solution

Because the lengths given are for the
adjacent side and the hypotenuse, the formula for $\cos\theta$ must be used.

$$\cos\theta = \frac{A}{H}$$

$$= \frac{8}{17} = 0.470588235$$

$$\theta = \cos^{-1}(0.470588235) = 61.92751306°$$

$$= 61.9° \quad \text{(to 1 decimal place)}$$

Example 3

A rectangle has sides of length 5 m and 10 m. Determine the angle between the long side of the rectangle and a diagonal.

Solution

The solution is illustrated in the diagram.

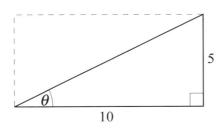

Using the formula for $\tan\theta$ gives

$$\tan\theta = \frac{5}{10}$$

$$= 0.5$$

Then using the $\tan^{-1}$ key on a calculator gives

$$\theta = \tan^{-1}(0.5) = 26.56505118°$$

$$= 26.6° \quad \text{(to 1 decimal place)}.$$

Exercises

1. Giving your answers, where necessary, correct to 1 decimal place, use your calculator to obtain θ if:

   (a) $\sin\theta = 0.8$ (b) $\cos\theta = 0.5$ (c) $\tan\theta = 1$

   (d) $\sin\theta = 0.3$ (e) $\cos\theta = 0$ (f) $\tan\theta = 14$

2. Use the tangent function to calculate the angle θ in each of the following diagrams. In each case, give your answer correct to 1 decimal place.

   (a) 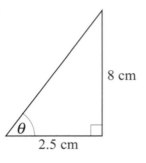   (b)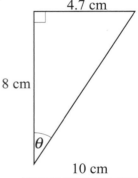

   (c) 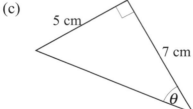   (d)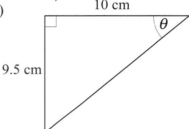

3. Use sine or cosine to calculate the angle θ in each of the following triangles. In each case, give your answer correct to 1 decimal place.

   (a) 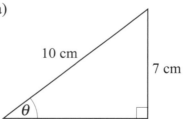   (b)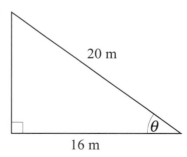

   (c) 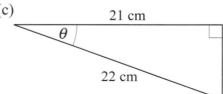   (d)

4. Calculate the angle θ in each of the following triangles. In each case, give your answer correct to 1 decimal place.

(a)
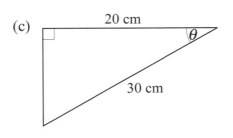

(b)
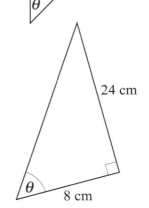

(c)

20 cm

(d)

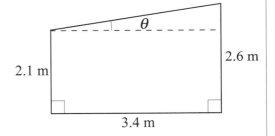

5. A right-angled triangle has sides of length 3 cm, 4 cm and 5 cm.

Determine the sizes of all the angles in the triangle, giving your answers to the nearest degree.

6. The diagram shows the cross-section of a shed.

Calculate the angle θ between the roof and the horizontal. Give your answer to the nearest degree.

2.1 m

2.6 m

3.4 m

7. A ladder of length 6 m leans against a wall. The foot of the ladder is at a distance of 3 m from the base of the wall.

Calculate the angle between the ladder and the ground.

8. A rectangle has sides of length 12 cm and 18 cm.

(a) Calculate the length of the diagonal of the rectangle, giving your answer to the nearest millimetre.

(b) Calculate the angle between the diagonal and the shorter side of the rectangle, giving your answer to the nearest degree.

9.   As an aeroplane travels 3000 m along a straight flight path, it rises 500 m.

      Calculate the angle between the flight path of the aeroplane and the
      horizontal. Give your answer to a sensible level of accuracy.

10.   A weight hangs from 2 strings as shown in the diagram.

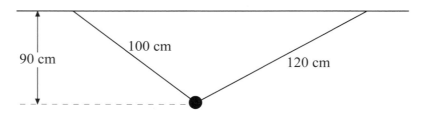

      Calculate the angle between the two strings, giving your answer to the
      nearest degree.

11.   Ramps help people going into buildings.

      A ramp that is 10 m long must not have a height greater than 0.83 m.

      (a)   Here are the plans for a ramp:

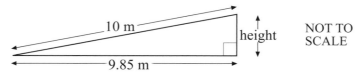

            Is this ramp too high?
            You *must* show calculations to explain your answer.

      (b)   Here are the plans for a *different* ramp.

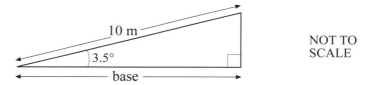

            How long is the base of this ramp?
            You *must* show your calculations.

      (c)   The recommended gradient of a ramp is 1 in 20.

            What angle gives the recommended gradient?
            You *must* show your calculations.

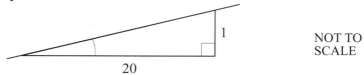

                                                          (KS3/99/Ma/Tier 6-8/P2)

12. A boat sails from the harbour to the buoy.
    The buoy is 6 km to the east and 4 km to the north of the harbour.

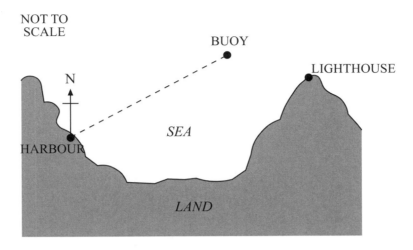

(a) *Calculate* the shortest distance between the buoy and the harbour.
    Give your answer to 1 decimal place.

    Show your working.

(b) *Calculate* the bearing of the buoy from the harbour.

    Show your working.

    The buoy is 1.2 km to the north of the lighthouse.
    The shortest distance from the lighthouse to the buoy is 2.5 km.

(c) *Calculate* how far the buoy is to the west of the lighthouse.

    Give your answer to 1 decimal place.

    Show your working.

    (KS3/96/Ma/Tier 6-8/P1)

13. Bargate is 6 km east and 4 km
    north of Cape Point.

    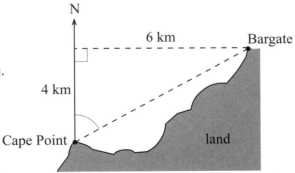

    (a) Steve wants to sail directly
        from Cape Point to Bargate.

        On what bearing should he
        sail?

        Show your working.

    (b) Anna sails from Cape Point
        on a bearing of 048 °.
        She stops when she is due north of Bargate.

        How far north of Bargate is Anna?
        Show your working.

    (KS3/98/Ma/Tier 6-8/P2)

16 Cumulative Frequency

16.1 Averages

In this section we revisit the three types of average, the *mean, median* and *mode*. We also use the *range* of a set of data.

$$\text{Mean} \quad = \quad \frac{\text{sum of the values}}{\text{number of values}}$$

Median = middle value (when the data is arranged in order); where there are two central values, the median is their mean

Mode = most common value

Range = difference between largest and smallest values

Example 1

1	7	8	2	3	6	5	10	3

For this sample,

(a) calculate the *mean*,

(b) determine the *median,*

(c) state the *mode,*

(d) calculate the *range*.

Solution

(a) Mean $= \dfrac{1 + 7 + 8 + 2 + 3 + 6 + 5 + 10 + 3}{9}$

$= \dfrac{45}{9}$

$= 5$

(b) To find the median, first write the numbers in order.

1   2   3   3   ⑤   6   7   8   10

↓

Median

As the number of data items is odd, the median will be the middle number, which is 5 in this case, so

Median = 5

(c) The mode is the most common value, which is 3 for this set of values.

(d) Range $= 10 - 1$

$= 9$

Example 2

Determine the *median* of the following set of values:

44   32   88   19   33   74   62   31   33   56

Solution

First write the numbers in order:

19   31   32   33   (33   44)   56   62   74   88

In this case, there are 2 middle numbers, 33 and 44. The median will be the mean of these.

$$\text{Median} = \frac{33 + 44}{2}$$

$$= \frac{77}{2}$$

$$= 38.5$$

Example 3

A class collected data on the number of people living in their home, which is shown in the following table:

Number of People Living in Home	Frequency
2	3
3	9
4	10
5	2
6	3
7	1
8	1
9	0
10	1

(a)   Calculate the *mean* number of people living in each home.

(b)   Determine the *median* of the data.

(c)   State the *mode* of the data.

Solution

(a)   The first step is to complete the table below:

Number of People Living in Home	Frequency	Number of People × Frequency
2	3	6
3	9	27
4	10	40
5	2	10
6	3	18
7	1	7
8	1	8
9	0	0
10	1	10
TOTALS	30	126

Mean $= \dfrac{126}{30}$

$= 4.2$ people per home

(b)   As there are 30 values, the median is the mean of the 15th and 16th values. From the first table we can see that both the 15th and 16th values are 4, so the median is 4 people per home.

(c)   The most common value is 4 so the mode is 4 people per home.

Exercises

1.   Calculate the *mean* and the *range* of each of the following sets of data:

(a)   3   17   5   6   12

(b)   30   42   19   21   33   62

(c)   7   8   3   14   31   3   8   9   13   22

(d)   114   115   110   119   114   118   123   133

2.   Determine the *median* and the *mode* of each of the following sets of data:

(a)   8   5   19   32   19

(b)   33   14   16   19   22   33   16   33   22

(c)   5   9   19   3   14   21   5   7

(d)   11   21   19   11   13   16   11   19   22   20

3. In which of the following data sets is the *mean* the same as the *median*:

    A   34   6   19   17   9

    B   29   12   17   18   44   13   17   40

    C   101 107 183 51   57   77   100 92

    D   27   92   56   83   45

4. Which of the following data sets has the *largest* range:

    A   14   27   88   73   56   61

    B   374 521 628 314 729

    C   888 912 897 907 887 893

5. The following table gives the results of a survey question asking people how many television sets they had in their home.

Number of Televisions	Frequency
0	3
1	18
2	64
3	73
4	22
5	14
6	6

    For this data,

    (a)   calculate the *mean,*

    (b)   determine the *median,*

    (c)   state the *mode.*

6. A car park manager recorded the number of cars entering her car park each hour. The data she collected is listed below.

    16   22   17   6   5   8   32   15   9   7   14   33

    21   11   6   5   11   14   12   22   19   11   3   14

    14   7   23   41   32   16   5   19   14   33   7   12

    For this data:

    (a)   calculate the *mean,*   (b)   determine the *median,*

    (c)   determine the *mode,*   (d)   calculate the *range.*

    Which of the 3 averages should the manager use to convince her employers that the car park is going to make a large profit?

7. John looks at the price of a computer game in 8 different shops. The prices he sees are:

       £29.99   £25.00   £34.99   £29.00

       £24.99   £29.99   £31.00   £29.95

    (a) Calculate the *mean* of this data.

    (b) State the *mode* of this data.

    (c) Determine the *median*.

    Which of these averages should he use to argue that the computer game is too expensive?

8. For the set of data given below, calculate the *mean* and determine the *median*.

       4   7   3   9   5   6   142   3   7   11

    Describe the advantages of using the median, rather than the mean in this case.

9. A student collected data on the number of visits to the dentist made by members of his class in one school year.

    His results are shown in the following bar chart:

    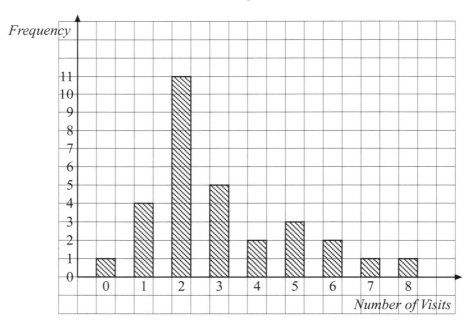

    For the data:

    (a) state the *mode,*

    (b) calculate the *mean,*

    (c) determine the *median*.

10. A set of three numbers has *mean* 11, *median* 12 and *range* 13. What are the 3 numbers?

16.2 Grouped Data

When dealing with grouped data it is important to think about the type of data that is being processed. You also have to decide the range of values that each group contains.

When calculating the mean of grouped data, we assume that all the values lie at the midpoint of the group.

These ideas are illustrated in the following examples.

Example 1

The table below shows the times taken by a group of walkers to complete a 15-mile walk. Their times have been recorded to the nearest hour.

Illustrate the data using a bar chart and a frequency polygon.

Time (hours)	3	4	5	6	7	8
Frequency	2	5	12	11	4	3

Solution

A time of 5 hours actually means a time that is greater than or equal to $4\frac{1}{2}$ hours but is less than $5\frac{1}{2}$ hours, so the bar representing this time on the bar chart will begin at 4.5 and end at 5.5.

Similarly, the bar for a time of 3 will begin at 2.5 and end at 3.5.

The bar chart is shown below:

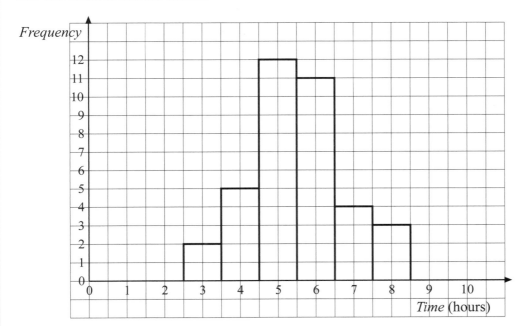

The frequency polygon is shown below. We obtain it by joining the midpoints of the tops of the bars from the previous graph.

Example 2

At a school fair, visitors enter a 'Guess the weight of the cake' competition. Their guesses, rounded to the nearest 100 grams, were recorded in the following table:

Guess (kg)	0.5 - 0.7	0.8 - 1.0	1.1 - 1.3	1.4 - 1.6	1.7 - 1.9
Frequency	5	32	26	11	6

(a) Illustrate the data using a bar chart.

(b) Estimate the mean of the data.

(c) State the modal class.

Solution

(a) The guesses have been recorded to one decimal place, in other words to the nearest 100 grams. This means that the first category, nominally described as '0.5 - 0.7 kg' actually includes guesses greater than or equal to 0.45 kg but less than 0.75 kg. The precise description of the first category is therefore

$$0.45 \text{ kg} \le \text{guess} < 0.75 \text{ kg}$$

The nominal descriptions of the other classes must also be interpreted precisely if we are to represent the data accurately.

Guess (kg)	$0.45 \le G < 0.75$	$0.75 \le G < 1.05$	$1.05 \le G < 1.35$	$1.35 \le G < 1.65$	$1.65 \le G < 1.95$
Frequency	5	32	26	11	6

The precise descriptions of the classes indicate how the bars should be drawn on the bar chart.

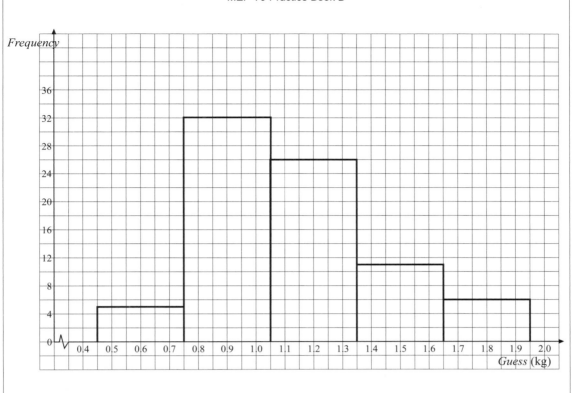

(b) The mean can be estimated by assuming that all the values in a class are equal to the midpoint of the class.

Class	Midpoint	Frequency	Frequency × Midpoint
$0.45 \le G < 0.75$	0.6	5	$5 \times 0.6 = 3$
$0.75 \le G < 1.05$	0.9	32	$32 \times 0.9 = 28.8$
$1.05 \le G < 1.35$	1.2	26	$26 \times 1.2 = 31.2$
$1.35 \le G < 1.65$	1.5	11	$11 \times 1.5 = 16.5$
$1.65 \le G < 1.95$	1.8	6	$6 \times 1.8 = 10.8$
TOTALS		80	90.3

$$\text{Estimate of mean} = \frac{90.3}{80} = 1.12875 \text{ kg}$$

$$= 1.1 \text{ kg} \quad \text{to 2 significant figures}$$

(c) The modal class is the one with the highest frequency. In this case, the modal class has nominal description '0.8 - 1.0 kg', which means guesses in the interval 0.75 kg $\le G < 1.05$ kg, i.e. 750 grams $\le G < 1050$ grams.

Exercises

1. The following table lists the results of a survey that recorded the heights of pupils in one year group. The heights have been given to the nearest 10 cm.

Height (cm)	140	150	160	170	180	190
Frequency	3	5	57	63	30	2

    (a) Illustrate the data on a bar chart.

    (b) Estimate the mean height of the pupils.

2. The following table lists the masses of a group of students, recorded to the nearest kg:

Mass (kg)	60	61	62	63	64	65	66	67	68	69	70
Frequency	3	7	9	11	10	22	17	23	11	9	5

    (a) Illustrate the data using a frequency polygon.

    (b) Estimate the mean mass for these students.

3. An English class looked at the number of words per sentence for an essay that one of them had written. Their results are summarised in the following table:

Number of Words	6 - 8	9 - 11	12 - 14	15 - 17	18 - 20
Frequency	13	10	8	4	3

    (a) Estimate the mean number of words per sentence.

    (b) What is the modal class?

4. The time taken for people to solve a puzzle is recorded, to the nearest minute, in the following table:

Time (mins)	2 - 5	6 - 9	10 - 13	14 - 17	18 - 21
Frequency	3	19	20	12	6

    Estimate the mean time taken to solve the puzzle.

5.   The bar chart shows the results of a survey into the height of 14-year-old pupils.

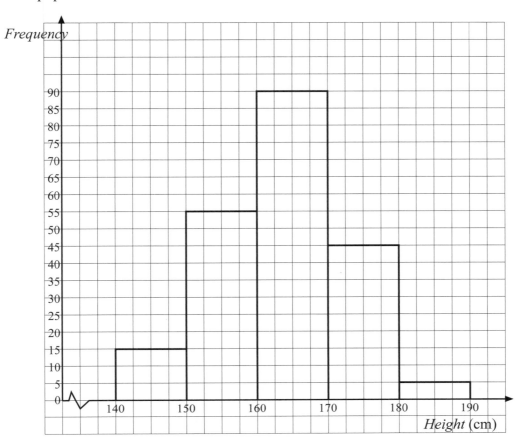

(a)   State the modal class.

(b)   Calculate an estimate of the mean height.

6.   The heights of some plants grown in a laboratory were recorded after 4 weeks. The results are listed in the following table:

Height (cm)	11 - 15	16 - 20	21 - 25	26 - 30	31 - 35	36 - 40
Frequency	3	7	19	20	11	2

(a)   Draw a frequency polygon for the data.

(b)   State the modal class.

(c)   Calculate an estimate of the mean height.

7. Estimate the mean of the data illustrated in the following frequency polygon:

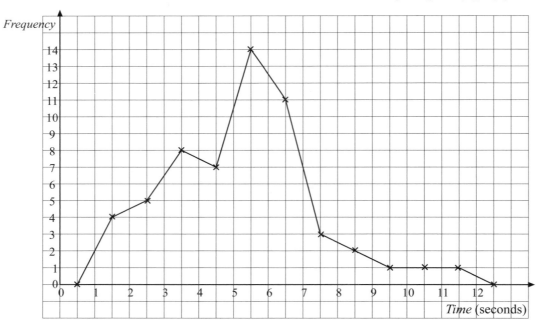

8. Children were asked to sell tickets for a school play. A record was kept of how many tickets each child sold.

Tickets Sold	0 - 10	11 - 20	21 - 50	51 - 100
Frequency	7	42	8	3

(a) Estimate the *mean* number of tickets sold.

(b) Estimate the *total* number of tickets sold.

9. A company owns a fleet of 20 vans. The mileage on each van is recorded. The results are given in the following table:

Mileage	$0 \leq M < 5000$	$5000 \leq M < 10\,000$	$10\,000 \leq M < 15\,000$	$15\,000 \leq M < 20\,000$
Frequency	1	4	8	7

(a) Illustrate the data with a bar chart.

(b) Estimate the mean mileage.

10. Joshua is given the data below and asked to estimate the mean.

Value	100 - 104	105 - 109	110 - 114	115 - 119
Frequency	5	16	32	7

(a) Calculate an estimate of the mean.

(b) Joshua also calculates that the mean must be greater than 107.9. Explain how he obtained this value.

(c) Determine a value that the mean must be less than.

11. Lyn recorded the temperature at lunch time every day for a week.
    She started to draw a bar chart to show her results.

    (a) The temperature on *Friday* was 25 °C.
        The temperature on *Saturday* was 19 °C.
        On a copy of Lyn's bar chart, draw the bars for *Friday* and
        Saturday.

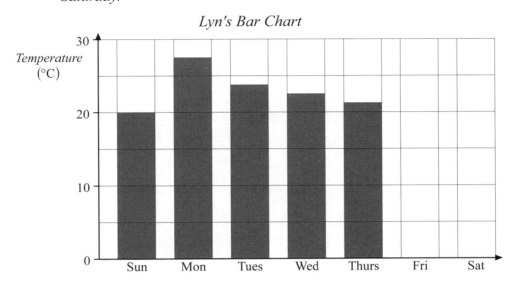

Lyn's Bar Chart

What was the temperature on *Monday*?

    (b) Five more pupils recorded the temperature every day for different
        weeks in the year.

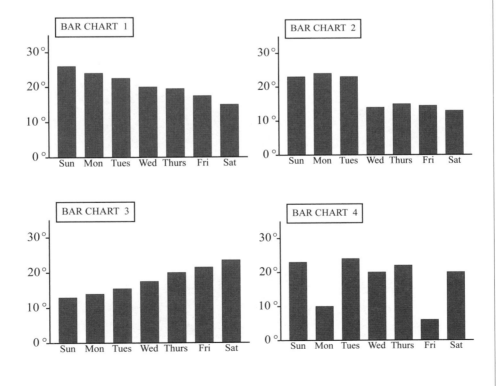

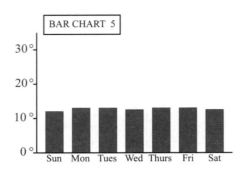

Match the pupils' comments to their bar charts. The first is done for you.

PUPILS' COMMENTS

Pupil A: *"It was very warm at first, then it suddenly got much colder."*

Pupil B: *"Each day was colder than the day before."*

Pupil C: *"The temperature was about the same all week."*

Pupil D: *"Each day was hotter than the day before."*

Pupil E: *"There were 5 warm days and 2 cold days."*

Pupil A: Bar Chart   2

Pupil B: Bar Chart ......

Pupil C: Bar Chart ......

Pupil D: Bar Chart ......

Pupil E: Bar Chart ......

(KS3/97/Ma/Tier 3-5/P2)

16.3 Cumulative Frequency

Cumulative frequencies are easy to calculate from a frequency table. Cumulative frequency graphs can then be used to estimate the median of a set of data. In this section we also look at the idea of *quartiles*, the *interquartile range* and the *semi-interquartile range*.

When you have a set of n values, in order,

$$\text{Lower quartile} \quad = \quad \frac{n+1}{4} \text{th value}$$

$$\text{Median} \quad = \quad \frac{n+1}{2} \text{th value}$$

$$\text{Upper quartile} \quad = \quad \frac{3(n+1)}{4} \text{th value}$$

$$\text{Interquartile range} \quad = \quad \text{upper quartile} - \text{lower quartile}$$

$$\text{Semi-interquartile range} \quad = \quad \frac{\text{interquartile range}}{2}$$

If the data is arranged in an ordered list, and the number of data values, n, is odd then the $\frac{n+1}{2}$ th value will be a single item from the list, and this will be the median. For example, if $n = 95$ the median will be the $\frac{95+1}{2} = 48$th value.

However, if n is even then $\frac{n+1}{2}$ will determine the two central values that must be averaged to obtain the median. For example, if $n = 156$ then $\frac{156+1}{2} = 78.5$, which tells us that we must average the 78th and 79th values to get the median.

For large sets of data, we estimate the lower quartile, median and upper quartile using the $\frac{n}{4}$ th, $\frac{n}{2}$ th and $\frac{3n}{4}$ th values. For example, if $n = 2000$, then we would estimate the lower quartile, median and upper quartile using the 500th, 1000th and 1500th values.

Example 1

For the following set of data,

4   7   18   3   9   5   10

(a) determine the *median,*

(b) calculate the *interquartile range,*

(c) calculate the *semi-interquartile range.*

Solution

First list the values in order:

3   4   5   7   9   10   18

(a) As there are 7 values, the median will be the $\dfrac{7+1}{2} = 4$th value.

Median = 7.

(b) The lower quartile will be the $\dfrac{7+1}{4} = 2$nd value.

Lower quartile = 4.

The upper quartile will be the $\dfrac{3(7+1)}{4} = 6$th value.

Upper quartile = 10.

$$\begin{aligned}
\text{The interquartile range} &= \text{upper quartile} - \text{lower quartile} \\
&= 10 - 4 \\
&= 6
\end{aligned}$$

$$\begin{aligned}
\text{The semi-interquartile range} &= \frac{\text{interquartile range}}{2} \\
&= \frac{6}{2} \\
&= 3
\end{aligned}$$

Example 2

(a) Draw a cumulative frequency graph for the following data:

Height (cm)	$150 \le h < 155$	$155 \le h < 160$	$160 \le h < 165$	$165 \le h < 170$	$170 \le h < 175$
Frequency	4	22	56	32	5

(b) Estimate the *median* from the graph.

(c) Estimate the *interquartile range* from the graph.

Solution

(a)   From the data table we can see that there are no heights under 150 cm.
       Under 155 cm there are the first 4 heights.
       Under 160 cm there are the first 4 heights plus a further 22 heights that are
       between 155 cm and 160 cm, giving 26 altogether.
       Under 165 cm we have the 26 heights plus the 56 that are between 160 cm
       and 165 cm, giving 82 altogether.
       Continuing this process until every height has been counted gives the
       following *cumulative frequency table*.

Height (cm)	Under 150	Under 155	Under 160	Under 165	Under 170	Under 175
Cumulative Frequency	0	0 + 4 = 4	4 + 22 = 26	26 + 56 = 82	82 + 32 = 114	114 + 5 = 119

The cumulative frequency graph can now be plotted using the points in the
table, (150, 0), (155, 4), (160, 26), (165, 82), (170, 114) and (175, 119).
To obtain the *cumulative frequency polygon,* we draw straight line sections
to join these points in sequence.

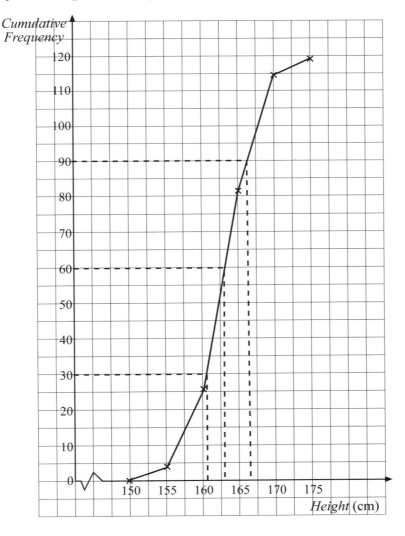

(b) There are 119 values, so the median will be the $\dfrac{119 + 1}{2} = 60$th value.

This can be read from the graph as shown above.

Median $\approx$ 163 cm.

The lower quartile will be given by the $\left(\dfrac{119 + 1}{4}\right)$th value.

Lower quartile $\approx$ 160.5 cm.

The upper quartile will be given by the $\dfrac{3(119 + 1)}{4}$th value.

Upper quartile $\approx$ 166.5 cm.

Using these values gives:

Interquartile range $= 166.5 - 160.5$

$= 6$ cm

Example 3

Estimate the semi-interquartile range of the data illustrated in the following cumulative frequency graph:

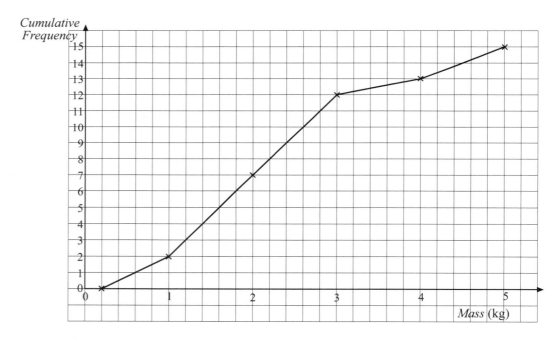

Solution

The sample contains 15 values, so the lower quartile will be the $\dfrac{15 + 1}{4} = 4$th value.

Similarly, the upper quartile will be the 12th value.

These can be obtained from the graph, as follows:

Lower quartile = 1.4 kg

Upper quartile = 3 kg

Interquartile range = 3 − 1.4

    = 1.6 kg

Semi-interquartile range = 0.8 kg

Exercises

1. Determine the median and interquartile range of the following set of data:

   11   8   5   9   7   3   4   8   14   16   2

2. Calculate the semi-interquartile range of this sample:

   42   26   32   41   52   33   88   71   38   52   53   27   46   32   59

3. In a sample, the semi-interquartile range is 14. The lower quartile is 5 less than the median. Determine the median if the upper quartile is 91.

4. Below are the times, in minutes, spent on homework one evening by a group of students.

Time Spent (min)	$0 \leq t < 10$	$10 \leq t < 20$	$20 \leq t < 30$	$30 \leq t < 40$	$40 \leq t < 50$
Frequency	3	7	10	15	4

(a)   Copy and complete the following cumulative frequency table:

Time (min)	Under 0	Under 10	Under 20	Under 30	Under 40	Under 50
Cumulative Frequency						

(b)   Draw a cumulative frequency polygon for this data.

(c)   Use the polygon to estimate the median.

(d)   Use the polygon to estimate the semi-interquartile range.

5.   Estimate the median and interquartile range of the data illustrated in the following cumulative frequency graph:

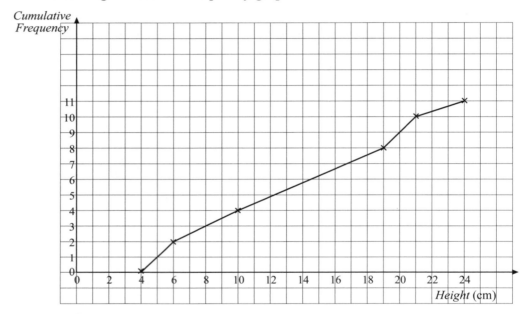

6.   (a)   Gather data on the height of the pupils in your class.

(b)   Draw a cumulative frequency graph for the data.

(c)   Use the graph to estimate the median height and the semi-interquartile range.

7.   Use a cumulative frequency graph to estimate the median and interquartile range of the following data:

Cost (£)	$10 \leq c < 11$	$11 \leq c < 12$	$12 \leq c < 13$	$13 \leq c < 14$	$14 \leq c < 15$
Frequency	8	12	40	2	1

8.   A factory collected data on the time for which a particular type of candle would burn. The data is summarised in the following table:

Time (mins)	$0 \leq t < 10$	$10 \leq t < 20$	$20 \leq t < 30$	$30 \leq t < 40$	$40 \leq t < 50$
Frequency	1	2	12	15	5

(a)   How do the mean and median compare?

(b)   Determine the semi-interquartile range for the data.

9.   The number of passengers on a bus route was recorded over a period of time, to give the following data:

Number of Passengers	Frequency
$0 \le n < 10$	3
$10 \le n < 20$	7
$20 \le n < 30$	12
$30 \le n < 40$	13
$40 \le n < 50$	29
$50 \le n < 60$	27

Determine the median and semi-interquartile range of the data.

10.   Give an example of a sample for which the semi-interquartile range is a quarter of the range of the sample.

11.   The cumulative frequency graph shows the height of 150 Norway fir trees.

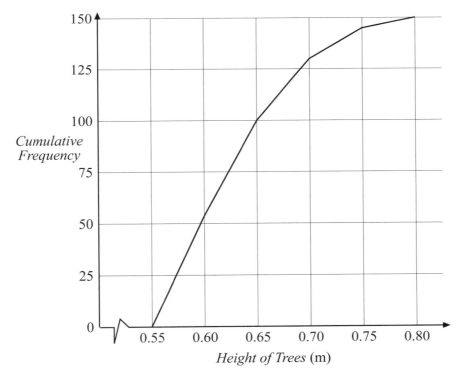

(a)   Use the graph to estimate the *median* height and the *interquartile range* of the Norway firs.

(b)   Which one of the following sketches of frequency diagrams shows the distribution of heights of the Norway firs?

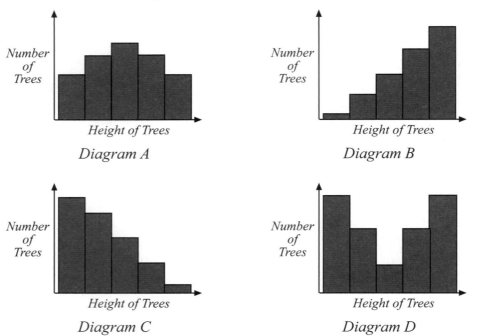

Diagram A

Diagram B

Diagram C

Diagram D

(KS3/98/Ma/Tier 6-8/P2)

12.   40 students worked on a farm one weekend. The cumulative frequency graph shows the distribution of the amount of money earned. No one earned less than £15.

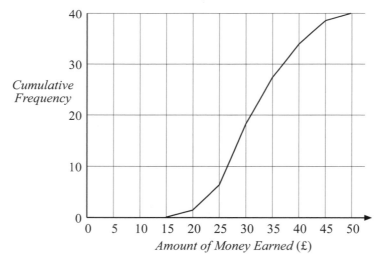

(a)   Read the graph to estimate the *median* amount of money earned.

(b)   Estimate the *percentage* of students who earned *less than £40*.

(c)   On a copy of the graph, show how to work out the *interquartile range* of the amount of money earned.

Write down the value of the interquartile range.

(d)   30 of the students work on the farm another weekend later in the
      year. The tables which follow show the distribution of the amount of
      money earned by the students.

Money Earned (£)	No. of Students	Money Earned(£)	No. of Students
≥ 25 and< 30	1	< 25	0
≥ 30 and < 35	2	< 30	1
≥ 35 and < 40	3	< 35	3
≥ 40 and < 45	4	< 40	6
≥ 45 and < 50	10	< 45	10
≥ 50 and < 55	7	< 50	20
≥55 and < 60	3	< 55	27
		< 60	30

Draw a cumulative frequency graph using a copy of the axes below.

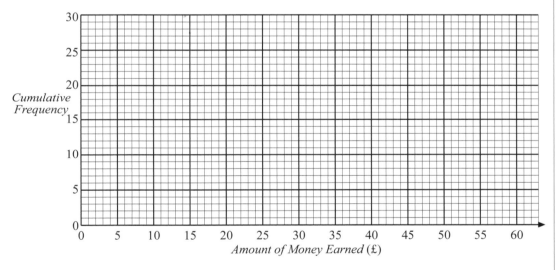

(e)   State whether each of the following statements is *true* or *false*.

   A.   Three of the students earned less than £35 each.

   B.   The median amount earned is between £40 and £45.

   C.   Most of the 30 students earned more than £50 each.

(KS3/97/Ma/Tier 6-8/P1)

16.4 Box and Whisker Plots

A box and whisker plot is based on the *minimum and maximum values*, the *upper and lower quartiles* and the *median*. This type of plot provides a good way to compare two or more samples.

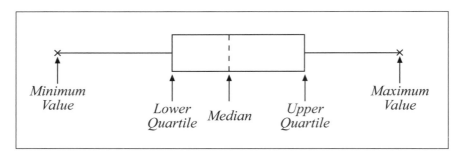

Note: Box and whisker plots must always be drawn accurately to scale.

Example 1

Given the information below, draw a box and whisker plot.

Minimum	82
Lower quartile	94
Median	95
Upper quartile	102
Maximum	110

Solution

The box and whisker plot is shown below.

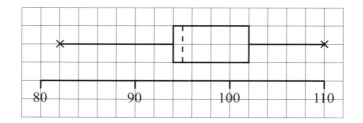

Example 2

Draw a box and whisker plot for this sample:

$$5 \quad 7 \quad 1 \quad 9 \quad 11 \quad 22 \quad 15$$

Solution

First list the sample in order, to determine the median and the quartiles.

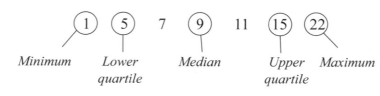

The box and whisker plot is shown below:

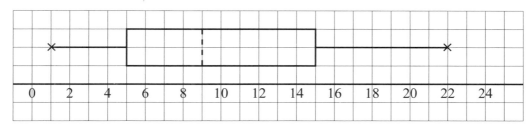

Example 3

A gardener collected data on two types of tomato. The box and whisker plot below shows data for the masses in grams of the tomatoes in the two samples.

Compare and contrast the two types and advise the gardener which type of tomato he should grow in future.

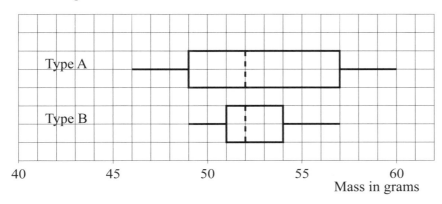

Mass in grams

Solution

	Type A	Type B
Median	52 grams	52 grams
Lower Quartile	49 grams	51 grams
Upper Quartile	57 grams	54 grams
Range	14 grams	8 grams
Interquartile Range	8 grams	3 grams

From this table we can see that both types of tomato have the same average mass because their medians are the same.

Comparing the medians and interquartile ranges shows that there is far more variation in the masses of the type A tomatoes, which means that the masses of type B are more consistent than those of type A.

However, comparing the two box and whisker plots, and the upper quartiles, shows that type A tomatoes will generally have a larger mass than those of type B.

Nevertheless, there will be some type A tomatoes that are lighter than any of type B.

Taking all this together, the gardener would be best advised to plant type A tomatoes in future as he is likely to get a better yield from them than from type B.

Exercises

1. Draw a box and whisker plot for a sample that has:

Minimum	10
Lower quartile	14
Median	16
Upper quartile	20
Maximum	29

2. Draw a box and whisker plot for the following sample:

17	22	18	33	14	36	39	41
25	31	18	19	16	21	21	

3. A sample has:

Minimum 3	Range 21
Semi-interquartile range 4	Median 17
Upper quartile 20	

   Draw a box and whisker plot for the sample.

4. For the sample illustrated in the following box and whisker plot, determine:

   (a) the range,   (b) the semi-interquartile range.

   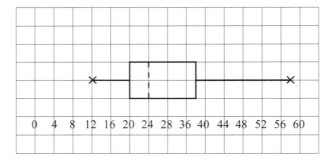

5. What are the median and the semi-interquartile range of the following sample:

   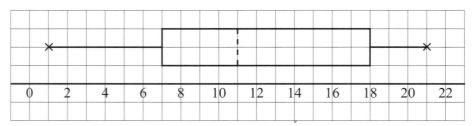

6. The two box and whisker plots show the data collected by the
    manufacturers on the life-span of light bulbs.

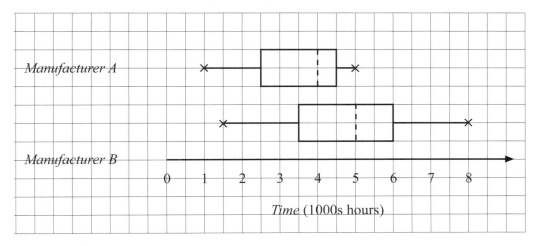

    From this data, which manufacturer produces the better light bulb?
    Give reasons for your answer.

7. A maths test is given to two classes. The results are illustrated below.
    Compare and contrast the results.

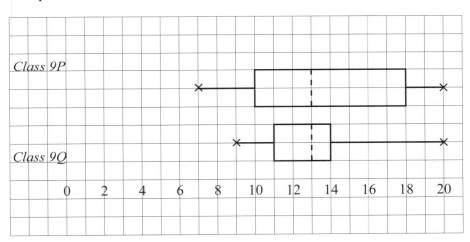

8. A builder can choose between two different types of brick that are coloured
    red or *yellow*. The box and whisker plots below illustrate the results of tests
    on the strength of the bricks.

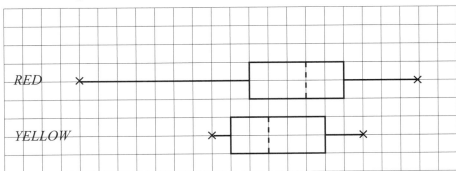

From the data illustrated in the box and whisker plots:

(a)   give one reason why the builder might prefer to use *red* bricks.

(b)   give one reason why the builder might prefer to use *yellow* bricks.

9.   A class took an English test and a Maths test. Both tests had a maximum possible mark of 25. The results are illustrated below.

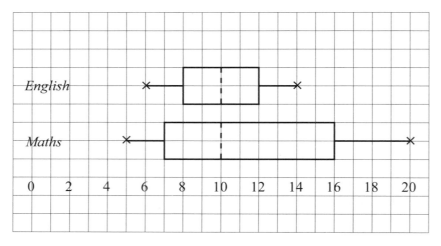

Compare and contrast the results.

10.   A cinema is showing 3 films, A, B and C. The ages of people watching the films are illustrated in the following box and whisker plots:

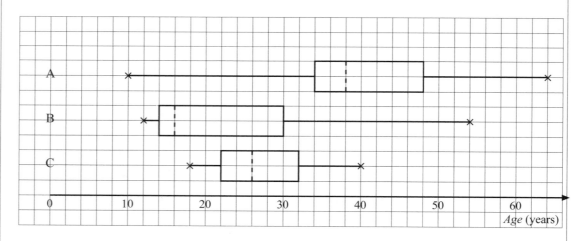

Answer the following questions, giving reasons to support your answers.

(a)   Which film do you think you would *not* be allowed to watch?

(b)   Which film would *you* probably enjoy most?

(c)   Which film would *your parents* probably enjoy most?

17 Quadratic Functions

17.1 Quadratic Expressions

In this section we revisit quadratic formulae and look at the graphs of quadratic functions.

The general formula for a quadratic graph is

$$y = ax^2 + bx + c$$

where a, b and c are constants. We investigate how varying the values of a, b and c changes the graph of the function.

Example 1

(a)   Draw the graph $y = x^2$.

(b)   Draw the graph $y = x^2 - 1$.

(c)   Sketch the graph $y = x^2 + 1$, describing how it relates to the graph $y = x^2$.

Solution

(a)   The following table gives a set of values that can be used to draw the graph:

x	-3	-2	-1	0	1	2	3
x^2	9	4	1	0	1	4	9

The graph is plotted opposite.

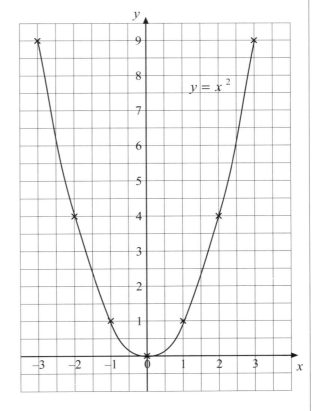

(b)   The table gives values for $y = x^2 - 1$.

x	-3	-2	-1	0	1	2	3
x^2	8	3	0	-1	0	3	8

Note that the graph $y = x^2$ is translated *downwards* 1 unit to give the graph $y = x^2 - 1$.

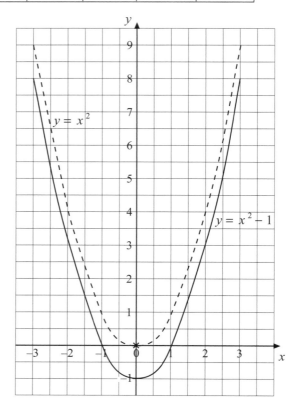

(c)   To obtain the graph $y = x^2 + 1$ the graph $y = x^2$ must be translated *upwards* by 1 unit, as shown in this diagram.

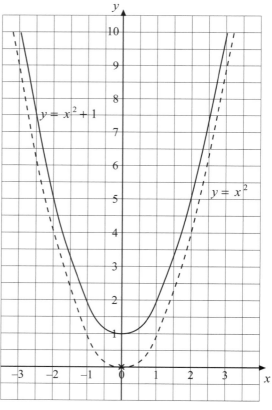

Example 2

(a) On the same set of axes, draw the graphs with equations,

$$y = x^2 \quad \text{and} \quad y = \frac{1}{2}x^2.$$

(b) Describe how the two graphs are related.

(c) Sketch the graphs $y = \frac{1}{4}x^2$ and $y = 2x^2$.

Solution

(a) The following table gives the values needed to plot the two graphs:

x	-3	-2	-1	0	1	2	3
x^2	9	4	1	0	1	4	9
$\frac{1}{2}x^2$	4.5	2	0.5	0	0.5	2	4.5

(b) The graph $y = \frac{1}{2}x^2$ always has exactly half the height of the graph $y = x^2$, as shown opposite.

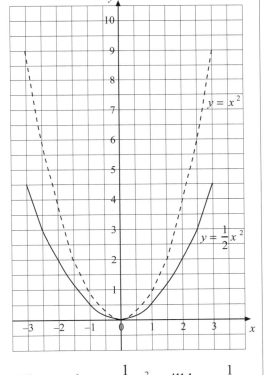

(c)

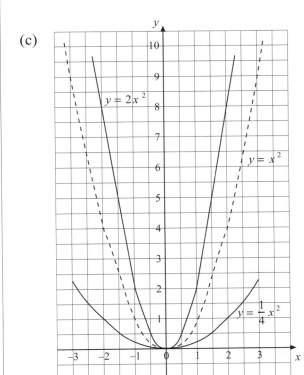

The graph $y = \frac{1}{4}x^2$ will have $\frac{1}{4}$ of the height of the graph $y = x^2$.

The graph $y = 2x^2$ will be twice as high as the graph $y = x^2$.

The two graphs are shown in the diagram on the left.

Exercises

In the following exercises you will explore further how the values of a, b and c change the shape of a quadratic graph.

1.   (a)   Draw the graph $y = x^2$.

       (b)   Draw the graph $y = x^2 + 3$ on the same axes.

       (c)   Draw the graph $y = x^2 - 2$ on the same axes.

       (d)   Describe how the three graphs are related.

2.   (a)   Draw the graph $y = -x^2$.

       (b)   On the same set of axes, draw the graphs:

            (i) $y = 4 - x^2$ (ii) $y = 9 - x^2$

            (iii) $y = 1 - x^2$ (iv) $y = -1 - x^2$

3.   On the same set of axes, sketch the graphs:

       (a) $y = x^2$ (b) $y = 3x^2$

       (c) $y = 4x^2$ (d) $y = \dfrac{3}{4}x^2$

4.   On the same set of axes, sketch the graphs:

       (a) $y = -x^2$ (b) $y = -\dfrac{1}{2}x^2$

       (c) $y = -\dfrac{1}{4}x^2$ (d) $y = -\dfrac{3}{4}x^2$

5.   (a)   Plot the graphs with equations,

            $y = 2x^2$ and $y = x^2 + 4$.

       (b)   What are the coordinates of the points where the two curves intersect?

6.   (a)   Draw the graphs with equations,

            $y = (x + 1)^2$, $y = (x + 3)^2$ and $y = (x - 2)^2$.

       (b)   Describe how each graph is related to the graph $y = x^2$.

       (c)   On a new set of axes, sketch the graphs with equations,

            $y = (x - 5)^2$, $y = (x - 3)^2$ and $y = (x + 4)^2$.

7.   Sketch the graphs with the following equations:

(a) $y = (x + 1)^2 + 1$ (b) $y = (x - 2)^2 - 3$

(c) $y = (x + 4)^2 - 3$ (d) $y = (x - 3)^2 + 2$

8.   (a)   Draw the graphs with equations,

$y = x^2 + x$, $y = x^2 + 2x$

$y = x^2 + 4x$, $y = x^2 + 6x$

(b)   For each graph, write down the coordinates of the lowest point. What would be the coordinates of the lowest point of the curve

$y = x^2 + bx$?

(c)   Draw the graphs of the curves with equations,

$y = x^2 - x$, $y = x^2 - 4x$ and $y = x^2 - 6x$

(d)   What would be the coordinates of the lowest point of the curve with equation $y = x^2 - bx$?

9.   (a)   Draw the graphs with equations,

$y = 2x^2 + 4x + 1$ and $y = 3x^2 + 6x + 2$.

(b)   Where does each curve intersect the y-axis?

(c)   Where does the curve $y = ax^2 + bx + c$ intersect the y-axis?

(d)   Write down the coordinates of the lowest point of each of the curves drawn in part (a).

(e)   What are the coordinates of the lowest point of the curve

$y = ax^2 + 2ax + c$?

10.   (a)   Plot the graphs,

$y = x^2 + 5x + 1$, $y = 2x^2 + 8x - 1$ and $y = 3x^2 - 9x + 7$.

(b)   What are the coordinates of the lowest point of the curve

$y = ax^2 + bx + c$?

11.   The graph shows the rate at which cars left a car park from 5 pm to 6 pm.

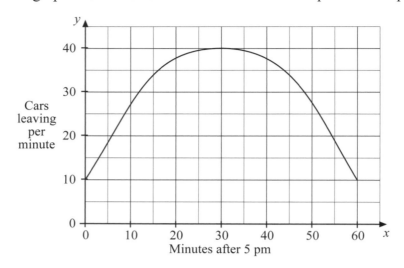

The lowest rate was 10 cars per minute at 5 pm and 6 pm.
The highest rate was 40 cars per minute at 5.30 pm.

$y = ax^2 + bx + c$ is the relationship between y, the number of cars leaving per minute, and x, the number of minutes after 5 pm.

(a)   Explain how you can work out from the graph that the value of c is 10.

(b)   Use the graph to form equations to work out the values of a and b in the equation $y = ax^2 + bx + c$.

Show your working.

(KS3/99/Ma/Ext)

17.2   Quadratic Equations: Factorisation

In this section we look at factorisation and how this can be used to solve quadratic equations. In Unit 11 you factorised expressions; we now take this one stage further to solve equations. In Unit 11 you looked at factorizing expressions with common factors. We now develop this to solving equations with common factors.

Example 1

Factorise: (a) $12x + 8$ (b) $x^3 + x^2$ (c) $3x^2 + 15x$

Solution

(a) $12x + 8 = 4(3x + 2)$

(b) $x^3 + x^2 = x^2(x + 1)$

(c) $3x^2 + 15x = 3x(x + 5)$

Example 2

Factorise: (a) $x^2 + 6x + 8$

(b) $x^2 - 5x + 6$

Solution

As both expressions contain x^2, they will factorise in the form:

$$(x \pm \square)(x \pm \square)$$

We must determine the missing numbers, and whether a '+' or a '−' sign is required in each bracket.

(a) For $x^2 + 6x + 8$ we require two numbers that multiply together to give 8 and add together to give 6.

So the numbers are 2 and 4.

Hence $x^2 + 6x + 8 = (x + 2)(x + 4)$.

$\times$	x	$+\,2$
x	x^2	$+2x$
$+\,4$	$+4x$	$+\,8$

(b) For $x^2 - 5x + 6$ we require two numbers that multiply together to give 6 and add together to give -5.

So the numbers are -2 and -3.

Hence $x^2 - 5x + 6 = (x - 2)(x - 3)$.

$\times$	x	$-\,2$
x	x^2	$-2x$
$-\,3$	$-3x$	$+\,6$

Example 3

Use factorisation to solve the following equations:

(a) $x^2 + 6x = 0$

(b) $x^2 + 3x + 2 = 0$

(c) $x^2 - 8x + 16 = 0$

Solution

(a) First factorise the quadratic expression

$$x^2 + 6x = 0$$

$$x(x + 6) = 0$$

For the left-hand-side to be zero, either:

$$x = 0 \quad \text{or} \quad x + 6 = 0$$

The second equation has solution $x = -6$, so the equation $x^2 + 6x = 0$ has solution $x = 0$ or $x = -6$.

(b) First factorise the left-hand-side of the equation:

$$x^2 + 3x + 2 = 0$$

$$(x + 2)(x + 1) = 0$$

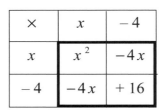

$$x + 2 = 0 \quad \text{or} \quad x + 1 = 0$$

so the equation $x^2 + 3x + 2 = 0$ has solution

$$x = -2 \quad \text{or} \quad x = -1$$

(c) Factorise the left-hand-side of the equation:

$$x^2 - 8x + 16 = 0$$

$$(x - 4)(x - 4) = 0$$

$$(x - 4)^2 = 0$$

So $x - 4 = 0$

which means that the equation $x^2 - 8x + 16 = 0$ has just one solution, namely

$$x = 4$$

Note that in this example the equation has only one solution.

Example 4

Solve the following equations:

(a) $2x^2 = 3x$ (b) $x^2 = 7x - 6$

Solution

(a) First, we rearrange the equation so that it has 0 on the right-hand-side. This first step is essential.

$$2x^2 = 3x$$

$$2x^2 - 3x = 0 \qquad \textit{Subtracting } 3x \textit{ from both sides}$$

Now we factorise the left-hand-side and solve the equation as we did in Example 2.

$$x(2x - 3) = 0$$

so $x = 0$ or $2x - 3 = 0$.

The second equation has solution $x = 1\frac{1}{2}$.

Therefore the equation $2x^2 = 3x$ has solution $x = 0$ or $x = 1\frac{1}{2}$.

(b) Again, the first step is to rearrange the equation so that it has 0 on the right-hand-side.

$$x^2 = 7x - 6$$

$$x^2 - 7x + 6 = 0 \qquad \textit{Subtracting } 7x \textit{ from both sides and adding 6 to both sides}$$

Now we factorise the left-hand-side and solve the equation.

$$(x - 1)(x - 6) = 0$$

so $\quad x - 1 = 0 \quad$ or $\quad x - 6 = 0$.

Therefore the equation $x^2 = 7x - 6$ has solution $x = 1$ or $x = 6$.

Exercises

1. Factorise the following:

   (a) $3x + 21$

   (b) $5x - 20$

   (c) $x^2 - x$

   (d) $x^2 + 6x$

   (e) $x^3 - x^2$

   (f) $8x + 20x^2$

   (g) $4x - 30x^2$

   (h) $5x + 16x^2$

   (i) $x^4 + x^2$

2. Factorise the following:

   (a) $x^2 + 4x + 3$

   (b) $x^2 - 3x + 2$

   (c) $x^2 - 5x - 14$

   (d) $x^2 - 21x + 20$

   (e) $x^2 + 12x + 35$

   (f) $x^2 - 10x + 25$

   (g) $x^2 - 11x + 30$

   (h) $x^2 - 2x - 63$

   (i) $x^2 - 14x + 48$

3. Solve the following equations:

   (a) $x^2 - 4x = 0$

   (b) $x^2 + 3x = 0$

   (c) $x^2 - 7x = 0$

   (d) $x - 4x^2 = 0$

   (e) $7x - 3x^2 = 0$

   (f) $2x^2 - 5x = 0$

4. Solve the following equations:

   (a) $x^2 - 8x + 12 = 0$

   (b) $x^2 + 2x - 8 = 0$

   (c) $x^2 + x - 6 = 0$

   (d) $x^2 + 3x - 4 = 0$

   (e) $x^2 - 8x + 15 = 0$

   (f) $x^2 - 11x + 18 = 0$

   (g) $x^2 - 6x - 27 = 0$

   (h) $x^2 + 10x + 21 = 0$

   (i) $x^2 - 16x - 17 = 0$

   (j) $x^2 + 17x + 60 = 0$

5. Solve the following equations:

    (a) $x^2 = 8x$ (b) $3x^2 = 4x$

    (c) $x^2 + 5x = 50$ (d) $x^2 + 70 = 17x$

    (e) $x^2 + x = 56$ (f) $x^2 = 14x + 51$

6.   (a)   Draw the graph of the curve with equation $y = x^2 + 2x - 3$.

       (b)   Use the graph to explain why the equation $x^2 + 2x - 3 = 0$ has *two* solutions.

7.   (a)   Draw the graph of the curve with equation $y = x^2 + 2x + 1$.

       (b)   How many solutions will the equation $x^2 + 2x + 1 = 0$ have?

       (c)   Check your answer to (b) by factorising $x^2 + 2x + 1$.

8.   Use a graph to explain why the equation $x^2 + 2x + 2 = 0$ has no solutions.

9.   A rectangle is 3 cm longer than it is wide. The width of the rectangle is w cm and the area is 10 cm^2.

    (a)   Explain why $w(w + 3) = 10$.

    (b)   Show that the equation in part (a) can be rewritten in the form $w^2 + 3w - 10 = 0$

    (c)   Solve the equation $w^2 + 3w - 10 = 0$.

    (d)   Explain why only one of the solutions to the equation $w^2 + 3w - 10 = 0$ can be applied to the given rectangle.

    (e)   State the dimensions of the rectangle.

10.   The surface area of this cuboid is 18 cm^2. Determine the volume of the cuboid.

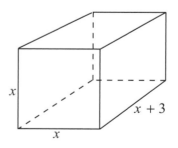

11.   Solve for y,

$$\frac{9}{y + 2} = y + 2$$

17.3 Quadratic Equations: Completing the Square

Completing the square is a useful technique for solving quadratic equations. It is a more powerful technique than factorisation because it can be applied to equations that do not factorise.

When completing the square, an expression like,

$$ax^2 + bx + c \text{ is written in the form } (Ax + B)^2 + C.$$

We will begin with the simple example where $a = 1$. In this case we will write expressions in the form

$$x^2 + bx + c \text{ as } (x + B)^2 + C$$

If we expand $(x + B)^2 + C$ we get $x^2 + 2Bx + B^2 + C$.

Comparing this with $x^2 + bx + c$ shows that

$$b = 2B \quad \text{and} \quad c = B^2 + C$$

which gives $B = \dfrac{b}{2}$ and $C = c - B^2$

Using these two results we can now set about completing the square in some simple cases.

Example 1

Write each of the following expressions in the form $(x + B)^2 + C$.

(a) $x^2 + 6x + 1$ (b) $x^2 + 4x - 2$ (c) $x^2 + 2x$

Solution

(a) Comparing $x^2 + 6x + 1$ with $x^2 + bx + c$ we see that $b = 6$ and $c = 1$ in this case, so

$$B = \frac{b}{2} = \frac{6}{2} = 3 \quad \text{and} \quad C = c - B^2 = 1 - 3^2 = -8.$$

Therefore $x^2 + 6x + 1 = (x + 3)^2 - 8$.

(b) Here $b = 4$ and $c = -2$, so

$$B = \frac{b}{2} = \frac{4}{2} = 2 \quad \text{and} \quad C = c - B^2 = (-2) - 2^2 = -6.$$

Therefore $x^2 + 4x - 2 = (x + 2)^2 - 6$.

(c) Here $B = \dfrac{2}{2} = 1$ and $C = 0 - 1^2 = -1$,

so $x^2 + 2x = (x + 1)^2 - 1$.

Example 2

Solve the following equations by completing the square.

(a) $x^2 - 4x - 5 = 0$ (b) $x^2 + 6x - 1 = 0$

Solution

(a) Completing the square gives,

$$x^2 - 4x - 5 = (x - 2)^2 - 9$$

Now we can solve the equation

$$(x - 2)^2 = 9$$

$$x - 2 = \pm \sqrt{9}$$

$$x - 2 = \pm 3$$

$$x = 2 \pm 3$$

so $x = 5$ or -1

(b) Completing the square gives,

$$x^2 + 6x - 1 = (x + 3)^2 - 10$$

Now we can solve the equation

$$(x + 3)^2 = 10$$

$$x + 3 = \pm \sqrt{10}$$

$$x = -3 \pm \sqrt{10}$$

so $x = 0.162$ or -6.162 to 3 decimal places

Exercises

1. Write each of the following expressions in the form $(x + B)^2 + C$.

    (a) $x^2 + 6x$ (b) $x^2 + 4x$

    (c) $x^2 + 8x$ (d) $x^2 - 10x$

    (e) $x^2 + 7x$ (f) $x^2 - 5x$

2. Write each of the following expressions in the form $(x + B)^2 + C$:

    (a) $x^2 + 6x + 1$ (b) $x^2 - 8x + 3$

    (c) $x^2 + 10x - 12$ (d) $x^2 + 12x + 8$

    (e) $x^2 - 4x + 1$ (f) $x^2 - 6x - 3$

    (g) $x^2 + 5x + 3$ (h) $x^2 + 3x - 4$

    (i) $x^2 + x - 2$ (j) $x^2 - x + 3$

3. Solve each of the following quadratic equation by completing the square:

    (a) $x^2 - 2x - 8 = 0$ (b) $x^2 + 4x + 3 = 0$

    (c) $x^2 + 8x + 12 = 0$ (d) $x^2 - 5x + 4 = 0$

    (e) $x^2 - 2x - 15 = 0$ (f) $x^2 + 3x - 28 = 0$

4. Solve each of the following quadratic equations by completing the square.
    Give your answers to 2 decimal places.

    (a) $x^2 + 2x - 5 = 0$ (b) $x^2 + 4x - 1 = 0$

    (c) $x^2 + 6x - 5 = 0$ (d) $x^2 - 10x - 1 = 0$

    (e) $x^2 + x - 3 = 0$ (f) $x^2 - 3x + 1 = 0$

    (g) $x^2 + 5x - 4 = 0$ (h) $x^2 + 3x - 5 = 0$

5. The rectangle shown has an area of 20 cm^2.

    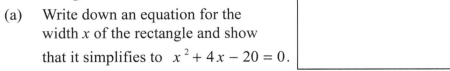

    (a) Write down an equation for the
         width x of the rectangle and show
         that it simplifies to $x^2 + 4x - 20 = 0$.

    (b) Use completing the square to determine the width of the rectangle to
         2 decimal places.

6. (a) Write the equation $x^2 - 8x + 18 = 0$ in the form $(x + B)^2 + C = 0$.

    (b) Explain why the equation has no solutions.

7. Simplify each of the following equations and obtain their solutions by completing the square.

    (a) $4x^2 + 20x - 8 = 0$ (b) $20x^2 - 40x + 60 = 0$

    (c) $3x^2 + 6x - 9 = 0$ (d) $5x^2 - 30x - 15 = 0$

8. The height of a ball at time t seconds can be calculated by using the formula

    $$h = 20t - 5t^2$$

    (a) Calculate the value of h when $t = 2$.

    (b) Determine the values of t for which $h = 15$.

9. The area of the rectangle shown is 30 cm^2.
    Determine the value of x.

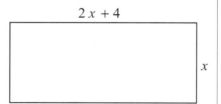

10. The area of the triangle shown is 120 cm^2.
    Determine the perimeter of the triangle correct to the nearest millimetre.

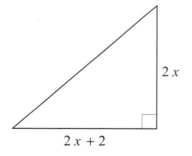

11. Use the method of completing the square or the appropriate formula to solve $x^2 + 4x - 2 = 0$.

    Show your working.

    Write your answers showing all the digits on your calculator.

    (KS3/95/Ma/Levels 9-10)

18 Sampling

18.1 Random Samples

In this section we look at random samples and at the difference between a *census* and a *sample*.

In a census, information on every member of a population is considered. In the UK, a census is carried out every 10 years. The amount of work required to carry out a census means that it is an expensive process.

In a sample, a subset of the population is considered to try to obtain information about a particular problem or issue. Because a sample is normally much smaller than the whole population, it is quicker and easier to take and to analyse a sample than to carry out a census of the entire population. Sampling entails less effort and less expense. In some cases, it is essential to take a sample. For example, imagine a firm that uses quality control to test the light bulbs it manufactures, to see how long they last. (If every item was tested until it stopped working they would have no light bulbs left to sell!) They therefore take samples from the production and test these to see if the quality is up to standard.

In a *random sample,* every member of the population is *equally likely* to be included in the sample. One way of selecting a sample is to use random numbers, as demonstrated in the example below. You can find random numbers in books of statistical tables. You can also generate them using a calculator or a computer.

The diagram shows part of a table of random digits.

Random Digits					
98859	09884	45275	09467	93026	32912
26604	95099	93751	00590	93060	64776
82984	65780	94428	30160	86023	52284
70888	14063	96700	83008	17579	71321
77803	61872	86245	68220	66267	01379
11304	01658	82404	46728	35228	49673
53552	51215	45611	83927	00772	99295

Example 1

In a class there are 30 pupils. The teacher decides to take a random sample of 5 pupils to estimate the mean height of the pupils in the class. Select a random sample of 5 pupils from the list.

1 Alan	10 Rachel	19 Sacha	28 Salif
2 Lucy	11 Ben	20 Halim	29 Annie
3 Tom	12 Emma	21 Daniella	30 Karen
4 Azar	13 Hannah	22 Joseph	
5 Jayne	14 Grace	23 Anna	
6 Nadima	15 Miles	24 Sophie	
7 Matthew	16 James	25 Kathryn	
8 Sushi	17 Joshua	26 Helen	
9 Mohammed	18 Lisa	27 Fatoumata	

Solution

To take a random sample you need to use a list of random digits, as follows:

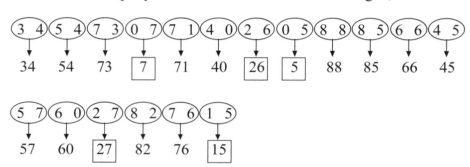

The digits are taken in pairs to form 2-digit numbers, as shown above. All those numbers greater than 30 are discarded (as there are 30 pupils on the list). The process is continued until 5 different numbers between 1 and 30 have been obtained.

So the sample will be made up of the following pupils:

7	Matthew
26	Helen
5	Jayne
27	Fatoumata
15	Miles

Example 2

Discuss whether or not the following situations produce random samples.

(a) Mark is conducting a survey for a magazine. He stops people at random on a Saturday morning at his local shopping centre.

(b) Granny Taylor's National Lottery numbers.

Solution

(a)   To produce a random sample, every member of the population must have an equal chance of being selected. In the case of Mark's sample, he is excluding people who are at work on that Saturday, as well as other people who haven't gone to that shopping centre. So although Mark is stopping people at random, he is not producing a random sample.

(b)   Most people use personal reasons when they select their National Lottery numbers. Granny Taylor may, for example, have used the number of grandchildren that she has, their birthdays, the number of her house, etc. If that is the case then she has not selected a random sample. However, if she bought a 'Lucky Dip' from her local shop then the computerised National Lottery till should have produced a random sample.

Note: For small populations it is relatively easy to produce a random sample. Simply number every member of the population, write those numbers on pieces of paper and put them into a hat or tombola. Mix them well and ask someone to pick out as many numbers as you need for your sample, then take the corresponding items from the population. This process clearly becomes unmanageable when we investigate large populations, which is why we tend then to use random number generators.

Exercises

When using random number tables in the following questions, work from left to right along the top row of numbers, then similarly along subsequent rows.

1.   Use the random digits below to select a second sample of 5 from the class in Example 1.

7 1 9 5 4 3 5 9 1 6 8 4 5 3 2 1 7 6 6 0 1 2 3 3 7 0 2 2

6 3 7 1 3 5 3 3 2 3 6 5 2 4 6 5 1 1 3 0 8 5 7 3 9 6 5 5

2.   Use the table of random numbers shown at the start of this unit to select a sample of 10 pupils from the list in Example 1.

3.   There are 10 competitors in an athletics event. Their names are:

Jimmy Jump	Harold Hammer	Tom Throw
Dick Discus	Harry Hop	Paul Putt
Sam Shot	Liam Long	Jake Javelin
Victor Vault		

(a)   Number the competitors from

1 Jimmy Jump   2 Harold Hammer   ....

10 Victor Vault

(b)   Use the following list of random digits to select a random sample of 3
       of the competitors for drug testing.

26	60	49	50	99	93	75	10
05	90	93	06	06	47	76	82
98	46	57	80	94	42	83	01
60	86	02	35	22	84	70	88

4.   A council wants to talk to the residents of a street to discuss a proposed
      traffic calming scheme. The houses in the street are numbered from 1 to 57.

      Use the list of random digits in question 1 to identify a random sample of
      10 of the houses for the council to visit.

5.   In another road the houses are numbered from 1 to 539.

      Use the list of random numbers in question 1 to identify a random sample of
      6 houses for the council to visit.

6.   A telephone directory has 250 pages. On each page there are 400 names.

      (a)   Describe how you could use random numbers to select a random
            sample from the telephone book.

      (b)   Explain why the sample is *not* a random sample from the whole
            population of the area.

7.   The ages, in years, of the members of a computer club are listed below.

Dee	12	Max	16	Ollie	18
Denise	14	Nazir	15	James	11
Tom	16	Jane	17	Hannah	14
Holly	11	Ferdi	11	Gemma	13
Richard	15	Kim	14	Nadia	16
Jai	13	Grant	12	Hugh	14
Victor	13	Juliette	13	Ben	13
Peter	14	Nigel	14	Ali	15

      (a)   Number the club members from 1 Dee, 2 Max, ... 24 Ali.

      (b)   Use the list of random digits in question 1 to generate a random
            sample of 5 club members and calculate the mean age for your
            sample.

      (c)   Use the list of random digits in question 1 *in reverse order* (i.e. 5 5
            6 9, etc.) to generate a second random sample of 5 club members.
            Calculate the mean age for this new sample.

      (d)   Compare the two samples and the two means.

8. (a) Describe the *advantages* of using a census rather than a sample.

    (b) Describe the *disadvantages* of using a census rather than a sample.

9. Mr May wants to know the mean IQ of the pupils in his class.
    Would you recommend that he uses a sample or a census?
    State which *you* would use, and explain why.

10. A large school has 1800 pupils. The headteacher wants to find out how far
     the pupils have to travel to school. Advise him whether to carry out a census
     or to use a sample. Explain why you give this advice.

18.2 Sampling Techniques

In this section we look at two further techniques for sampling: *systematic* sampling
and *quota* sampling.

A systematic sample is taken by sampling at regular intervals.

A quota sample is when the different categories that make up the population are
represented according to their proportion within the overall population.

A typical use of quota sampling is in opinion poll surveys where there is a need to
reflect the way the population breaks down between the two genders, into different
age groupings, into cultural and ethnic backgrounds, etc. The choice of people
selected from each category is left to the person collecting the information.

We will use the class from Example 1 at the beginning of this unit to demonstrate
how to use these sampling techniques. The names are listed again below:

1	Alan	10	Rachel	19	Sacha	28	Salif
2	Lucy	11	Ben	20	Halim	29	Annie
3	Tom	12	Emma	21	Daniella	30	Karen
4	Azar	13	Hannah	22	Joseph		
5	Jayne	14	Grace	23	Anna		
6	Nadima	15	Miles	24	Sophie		
7	Matthew	16	James	25	Kathryn		
8	Sushi	17	Joshua	26	Helen		
9	Mohammed	18	Lisa	27	Fatoumata		

Example 1

Select a systematic sample of size

(a)   6   (b)   5

from the class.

Solution

(a)   As there are 30 pupils in the class, and we want a sample of 6, we calculate
      $30 \div 6 = 5$. We can then obtain our sample of size 6 by selecting every 5th
      member of the class.

      This would give:

5	Jayne
10	Rachel
15	Miles
20	Halim
25	Kathryn
30	Karen

(b)   For a sample of size 5 we could select every 6th member of the class:

6	Nadima
12	Emma
18	Lisa
24	Sophie
30	Karen

You can select a systematic sample of size 6 by choosing any of the first 5 items as
a starting point and then taking every 5th item thereafter. For example, in part (a)
we could have started with pupil number 2 (Lucy) and then selected pupils number
7, 12, 17, 22 and 27. This would have generated the sample

      Lucy, Matthew, Emma, Joshua, Joseph, Fatoumata.

Similarly, starting with pupil number 4 (Azar) in part (b) would have generated the
sample

      Azar, Rachel, James, Joseph, Salif.

Example 2

Create a quota sample of size 10 from the class.

Solution

Note that the class contains 12 boys and 18 girls.

As the ratio of boys to girls is 2 to 3 in the class, they must be in the same ratio in
the sample.
So for a sample of 10 we need 4 boys and 6 girls. These do not need to be chosen

at random, and so could be:

Alan	Lucy
Tom	Jayne
Azar	Nadima
Matthew	Sushi
	Rachel
	Emma

If the teacher is selecting the pupils then it is possible that they may choose their favourite 4 boys and 6 girls, which would introduce some bias to the sample. It is best to avoid this possibility by selecting 4 boys randomly from the group of 12 boys, likewise for the girls. This produces a *stratified random sample.* We will look at stratified random samples in more detail in section 18.3

Exercises

1. Select a systematic sample of size 10 from the class used in Example 1.

2. There are 400 trees in a plantation. All the trees have been planted in rows. Describe how to create a systematic sample of 25 trees.

3. The houses in a street are numbered from 1 to 340.
   Describe how to create a systematic sample of size 20.

4. A theatre group has 40 members of whom 15 are boys. A quota of size 8 is to be interviewed. How many girls and how many boys should be included in the sample?

5. Is a quota sample also a random sample?

6. Explain why a systematic sample is *not* a random sample.

7. A company employs the following numbers of staff in 3 categories:

Management	10
Technical	20
Administrative	20

   How many from each category should be included in a quota sample of size:

   (a)   10   (b)   5   (c)   25 ?

8.   Refer to the members of the computer club in question 7 of Exercise 18.1.
      Create systematic samples of size:

      (a)   8   (b)   6   (c)   4

      from the list of members.

9.   In a street the homes numbered 1 to 70 are houses and those numbered 71 to
      90 are bungalows.

      (a)   Which home numbers would you include in a systematic sample of
            size 18 ?

      (b)   How many bungalows would you include in a quota sample of
            size 18 ?

      (c)   Comment on the number of bungalows included in each sample.

10.   For the homes described in question 9, use the random number generator on
      a calculator or computer to create a random sample of size 18.

      How does the number of bungalows included in *this* sample compare with
      the samples used in question 9 ?

18.3 Stratified Random Samples

A stratified random sample is similar to a quota sample. The key difference is that
the representatives from each category are chosen at random. In the previous
section we looked at a quota sample that was made up of 4 boys and 6 girls.

In the *quota sample* the first 4 boys from the list were chosen and then the first
6 girls.

In a *stratified random sample* the 4 boys should be selected randomly from the 12
boys in the class. In the same way, the 6 girls should be selected randomly from
the 18 girls in the class.

Example 1

Take a stratified random sample of size 5 from the class considered in the earlier
sections.

Solution

The class consists of 18 girls and 12 boys, 30 pupils altogether. We want a sample

of size 5 so we need to include $\dfrac{5}{30} = \dfrac{1}{6}$ of the girls, and $\dfrac{1}{6}$ of the boys. This

means that we need to choose 3 girls and 2 boys.

We choose a random sample of 3 girls. The girls in the class are:

1	Lucy	7	Hannah	13	Sophie
2	Jayne	8	Grace	14	Kathryn
3	Nadima	9	Lisa	15	Helen
4	Sushi	10	Sacha	16	Fatoumata
5	Rachel	11	Daniella	17	Annie
6	Emma	12	Anna	18	Karen

Using random digits gives:

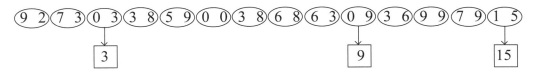

So the sample will contain:

3	Nadima
9	Lisa
15	Helen

The boys are:

1	Alan	5	Mohammed	9	Joshua
2	Tom	6	Ben	10	Halim
3	Azar	7	Miles	11	Joseph
4	Matthew	8	James	12	Salif

Using random digits gives:

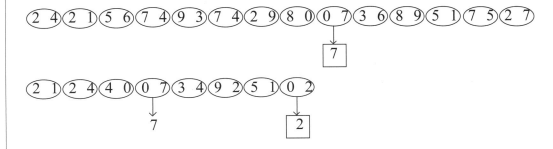

Note that the second 7 is ignored.

So the sample will also contain:

7	Miles
2	Tom

The complete stratified random sample will therefore consist of

Nadima, Lisa, Helen, Miles and Tom.

Example 2

A company has a total of 360 employees in four different categories:

Managers	36
Drivers	54
Administrative Staff	90
Production Staff	180

How many from each category should be included in a stratified random sample of size 20 ?

Solution

To create a sample of size 20 we need $\dfrac{20}{360}$ or $\dfrac{1}{18}$ of the workforce. So we take this fraction of the number of employees in each category.

Managers	$\dfrac{1}{18} \times 36$	= 2
Drivers	$\dfrac{1}{18} \times 54$	= 3
Administrative Staff	$\dfrac{1}{18} \times 90$	= 5
Production Staff	$\dfrac{1}{18} \times 180$	= 10
	TOTAL	= 20

Exercises

1. Create a stratified random sample of size 10 for the class considered in the Examples.

2. A catering company employs the staff listed in the following table:

Delivery Drivers	12
Cooks	36
Cleaning Staff	4
Sales Staff	8

    How many of each category of staff should be included in a stratified random sample of size 15 ?

3. A garage services VW and Audi cars. They want to carry out a customer satisfaction survey.

   (a) Explain why they might want to use a stratified random sample.

   (b) They have 2000 regular customers of whom 650 have Audi cars. Describe how to obtain a stratified random sample of size 40 of the customers to interview.

4. A farmer owns 120 Jersey cows and 180 Friesians. How many of each breed of cow should he include in a stratified random sample of 50 for a survey of milk quality?

5. A survey was carried out to determine the size people would prefer for a new coin. In the survey people were asked to select the size coin they preferred and indicate their sex by using the letter M or F.

   Forty people took part and the results are shown below.

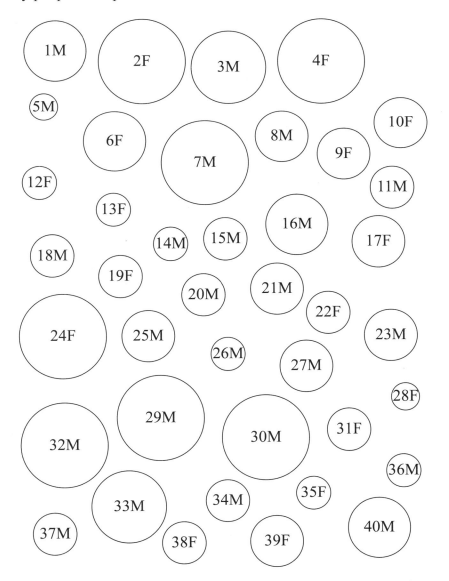

(a) How many males and how many females would you include in a stratified random sample of size 10 ?

(b) Select a stratified random sample of size 10 and use it to estimate the mean diameter of the coins.

6. There are 1200 pupils in a school. Their methods of transport to school are given below.

Bus   720

Walk   310

Cycle   90

Car   80

How many pupils from each category should be included in a stratified random sample of size 50?

7. There are 1500 homes in one part of a city. These homes can be divided into 3 categories:

Privately owned homes   720

Homes rented from council   592

Homes rented from private landlords   188

The council is to carry out a survey into the quality of homes.

(a) What would be the advantage of using a stratified random sample?

(b) How many homes of each type should be included in a stratified random sample of size 200 ?

8. (a) Find out how each member of your class travels to school.

(b) Create a stratified random sample of size 10.

(c) Find the time that it takes each of the people in the sample to travel to school.

(d) Calculate the mean time for your sample.

(e) Compare your results with other people's samples.